Money is *Not* the Cure

MARCH 2006

ENJOY!

Seymour Handler

MONEY IS *Not* THE CURE

Controversies in Healthcare

Seymour Handler, M.D.

Beaver's Pond Press, Inc.
Edina, Minnesota

ISBN-13: 978-1-59298-133-5
ISBN-10: 1-59298-133-X

Library of Congress Catalog Number: 2005938011

Printed in the United States of America

First Printing: January 2006

10 09 08 07 06   5 4 3 2 1

Beaver's Pond Press, Inc.

7104 Ohms Lane, Suite 216
Edina, MN 55439
(952) 829-8818
www.BeaversPondPress.com

To order, visit *www.BookHouseFulfillment.com*
or call 1-800-901-3480. Reseller discounts available.

Three fellow pathologists have been major contributors to my medical career. Their influences differ, but nevertheless, complement each other.

Dr. Donald F. Gleason, the internationally famous developer of the Gleason Prostate Cancer Histologic Grading System, was a major intellectual stimulus during my residency training at the Minneapolis VA Hospital. He taught me to doubt accepted dogma and stimulated me to contribute to the medical literature.

Dr. Ellis S. Benson, the retired Chairman of the Department of Laboratory Medicine and Pathology of the University of Minnesota Medical School, profoundly influenced my involvement in medical education. He gave me free reign in teaching pathology to medical students and also stimulated my sabbatical leaves to the Royal London Hospital in England.

Dr. Thomas T. Semba, unfortunately deceased many years ago, was my senior associate in pathology practice. He had a profound influence on me in personal integrity and morality, without which my rough edges would have been a significant detriment to professionalism.

I wish to acknowledge the outstanding support of the word processing section and personnel in the Medical Library of North Memorial Medical Center, without whom this work could not have been accomplished.

Contents

Introduction

One of our society's greatest problems in healthcare is managing costs. In recent years, healthcare has experienced double-digit cost inflation, a rate several times as high as that of the general inflation. Some of the inflation can be explained by changes in medical technology; modern medical practice includes many activities unknown just a few years ago. These changes, particularly advances in imaging procedures, cardiology interventions, orthopedic joint replacement, and treatment options in ophthalmology tend to be expensive. Comparing healthcare costs to those of a gallon of gasoline or a quart of milk is misleading. It is akin to comparing the price tags of new models of Cadillac automobiles to that of a one-speed bicycle.

In an earlier era, during contract negotiations between employers and employees, management often offered expanded health insurance benefits in lieu of higher wages. At the time, health insurance was relatively inexpensive; a company could cover retirees in addition to active employees. As healthcare became more costly, purchasing insurance for employees became an increasingly expensive venture, so much so that business was forced to reduce health insurance benefits.

Within the past two years, we have witnessed very difficult labor contract negotiations, up to and including strike actions, in which the major hotly debated issue was health insurance coverage. In fact, some of the older American industries, now in deep financial trouble, attribute their fiscal problems to the cost of health insurance. This cost is less onerous in startup companies that have not yet bargained away the store.

General Motors' recent financial troubles are due in part to the amount it spends on insurance for current employees and retirees. Estimates suggest that GM spends, for each manufactured automobile, fifteen hundred dollars on employee health insurance. This contributes to their current difficulty competing in the world's automobile market. A

1

recent brief report in *USA Today* emphasizes the GM problem dramatically. A worker in his mid-fifties was interviewed during his cigarette break outside the plant. He admitted to experiencing ongoing health problems, including diabetes, hypertension, and elevated serum cholesterol. He had already had quadruple coronary bypass graft surgery several years earlier. Laughing, he admitted that he also ate too many steaks.

This may be the classic example of the mismatch between money spent on healthcare and the lack of benefit.. This automobile worker is sitting on a time bomb—with a cigarette in his hand. He has three major coronary risk factors, and the bypass surgery will not likely help him live longer. The worst thing he can do is continue smoking cigarettes. Instead of attending adequately to his serious coronary risk factors, modern medical care subjected him to coronary bypass surgery costing GM over one hundred thousand dollars. This expensive surgery will likely do little for him in the long run. It will be a miracle if he survives to sixty. Very clearly, neither society nor the worker will benefit from this heavy healthcare expense.

We have substituted expensive medical technology for the inexpensive, carefully considered care of an earlier era. Instead of advising this patient to clean up his lifestyle, we perform an operation, the long-term value of which is seriously in question. As I indicated in my writing on the "mustard plaster" decades ago, we do too much in medical care, with scant attention to the benefit of the patient.[1] So much of current medical practice is procedure oriented, "doing" things for the sake of the activity, rather than considering whether or not the patient benefits from the busywork.

Deciding if expensive procedures truly pay off is the key to financing healthcare. My view is that patients don't benefit enough to make the expense worthwhile, not by a long shot. My position is decidedly contrarian. Most people believe firmly and sincerely that if we spend more resources and energy on healthcare, the health of the people will improve correspondingly. This widespread belief, which I find strange, is behind the frightening inflation of healthcare costs.

Most of the national discussion addresses how to finance healthcare. Solutions include increased expenditures, universal health insurance, a single payor system, better preventive medicine, expanded information infrastructure, and more effective administration. All of the above are appropriate potential improvements. However, no one considers the benefits we get given what we pay. Physicians and members of the government, the media, and the public all agree that healthcare is worth whatever it costs and that if we spend more on healthcare and medical research, people's health will continue to improve. But is this conclusion correct? Does more care mean better care?

These questions and society's answers date back many years. During the Lyndon Johnson Administration in the 1960s, Michael Debakey of Baylor University proposed a *Heart, Cancer, and Stroke* program, ostensibly to wipe out these serious diseases afflicting Americans. Some forty-five or fifty years later, these diseases continue to be a problem, despite huge expenditures.

The problem of healthcare cost inflation has now extended beyond health insurance costs. One commonly quoted figure indicates that healthcare in 1970 amounted to five percent of the gross national product (GNP); thirty-three years later, healthcare costs amount to more than 15 percent of a much larger GDP. Combining the percentage increase with the large increase in GDP might imply a ten to fifteen-fold increase in absolute costs.

Cost-benefit evaluation of healthcare must examine two parameters, life expectancy and quality of life. There is no doubt that healthcare in the United States costs a great deal more than it does in other comparable nations. By most comparisons and despite spending a great deal more money, life expectancy in the United States is about the same as in other Western democracies. Quality of health is a far more subjective parameter than is life expectancy; the latter is an easily calculated actuarial figure. Assessing quality means examining the ability to function well in employment, recreation, daily living, etc. If people have chronic illnesses, their quality of life is impaired. Modern medicine has demonstrated impressive improvements in technology that can improve life quality. Several medical specialties can be singled out for providing major advances in quality. In the field of orthopedics, weight-bearing joint replacements are now commonplace, improving function and relieving pain in older persons suffering from degenerative joint disease. Similarly ophthalmology has developed major technological advances, enabling the retention or improvement of vision in millions of people. Cardiology has experienced a revolution in interventional techniques, introducing coronary artery bypass graft surgery, angioplasties, and the correction of dysrhythmias. These cardiac interventions, although frightfully expensive, improve patients' symptoms for extended periods, though whether the patients live longer remains debatable. Other medical specialties boast similar but possibly less obvious technical advances.

Much of the impressive progress in medical science over the past few decades has been in basic science. The mapping of the human genome, the improved understanding of the immune mechanism, the clarification of chromosomal disorders, cloning, stem cell research, etc., are regularly discussed on the six o'clock television news and are often described as "amazing breakthroughs," and "sensational advances." Unfortunately, translating these advances in basic science to human disease therapy will take decades, despite the media hoopla and our unrealistic expectations. I was in active community hospital pathology practice for forty years and heard of these "advances" regularly. However, I rarely saw them translated into improved patient care.

One of the most unfortunate aspects of advancing medical technology, in addition to its contribution to cost inflation, is the tendency to introduce new procedures into everyday medical practice before appropriate safety and efficacy evaluation. The American way—with its need for bigger, better, and faster things—drives these tendencies, resulting in great expenditures and unrealistic expectations. The desire for financial gain spurs on these premature introductions. Rather than wait for the appropriate studies to support the value of the new technology, we act on the drive to make a profit, resulting in the proliferation of expensive procedures, many of which eventually are demonstrated to have little value and are abandoned. In the meantime, unfortunately, the hasty introduction of technology into everyday practice drives up costs but doesn't improve care.

As the reader will appreciate, this book will emphasize that the increasing cost of healthcare is not commensurate with the benefits patients receive in either quality of health or life expectancy. Some of the following chapters relate the inflation of costs directly to excessive care. For example, the sections on "progress" against cancer and cancer screening describe specific oncology (i.e., cancer) practices that are expensive but that benefit the patient modestly or not at all.

The section on the possible environmental causes of human disease addresses the relation between cost and benefit less directly. However, the reader will benefit at least intellectually by recognizing the relative lack of a relationship between general environmental pollution and disease. It pays to be better educated about how an individual's "personal" pollution is the predominant cause of disease.

Similarly, the section on dietary supplements emphasizes how the abundant consumption of supplements doesn't pay. This chapter emphasizes that an ordinary balanced diet is as useful in promoting health as anything purchased in the health food stores or drugstores.

The section on evidence-based medicine may be directed more at physicians than the general public, although it is vital that patients appreciate how little of medical practice is based on science. This section, an exposé about how much medicine avoids or ignores science, should stimulate patients to question a physician's recommendations in terms of demonstrated anticipated benefit.

The section on "real" preventive medicine attempts to demonstrate that the interests of patients are better served by their improving their lifestyles rather than seeking the busywork currently in vogue in the annual physical examination.

The content of this book derives from a course offered to seniors of the Elder Learning Institute, a function of the University of Minnesota. The course, entitled "Controversies in Healthcare," consisted of a series of lectures on different medical subjects, each covering content readily described as "controversial." My hope is that the reader, in addition to being stimulated by their "controversial" nature, will find the following chapters informative and enlightening.

References

1. S. Handler, "Bring Back The Mustard Plaster," *Minn Med* 54, (Dec 1971): 973-9.

1

Life Expectancy, Life Span, & The Limits of Medicine

The issue of life expectancy rarely arises in everyday medical practice. The physician-patient relationship involves an implied contract, in which the physician advocates for the patient's healthcare needs, generally without regard to age or life expectancy. The physician treats one patient at a time, not a whole population. Even the goals of medical care—to prolong life and to improve the quality of health—give scant attention to how long a person can reasonably expect to live. Yet, with life expectancy and quality of life at the center of the contract between physician and patient, physicians should consider longevity. How long can we expect to extend a person's life? What are the medical limits of doing so? Modern medicine appears to have unlimited technology, much of which does little to extend life or its quality significantly. Its use just raises the cost of medical care and benefits the patient very little. This point is critical in considering the current inflation of healthcare costs. We may be doing far too much for many patients, with little benefit commensurate with the costs.

Significant variability exists among physicians about how much care they ought to provide to patients. Some physicians refuse to recognize the limits of what they can do medically for their patients. As a result, the dying process is prolonged, without real benefit for the patient and at great cost to society. Others, perhaps with greater insight into the limits of medicine, emphasize supportive comfort for their dying patients. This minimizes the duration of the dying process. They do less, but in the broader sense they may be accomplishing far more in terms of patient dignity and comfort. Perhaps all physicians should have a greater appreciation of life expectancy, so that the limits of medicine are more clearly defined.

LIFE EXPECTANCY

Definition

Life expectancy at birth is defined as the average age of death in a population in a given time interval, usually one year. Since the United States Death Registration System was founded in 1900, most life expectancy comparisons cover the past century. Because the age at death is included in all death certificates, we can readily calculate life expectancy at birth. The calculation does not depend on the reliability of the cause of death of individuals. This calculation is a simple task, unrelated to the cause of death. The value of life expectancy information is particularly useful in evaluating both the health trends over the years and the adequacy of the healthcare system.

Although life expectancy at birth is the most widely quoted figure, life expectancy data is available at any age and for either sex. This information is very useful for identifying and understanding the segments of our society whose life expectancy has improved the most over the past century. Some examples will prove this point. Life expectancy at birth increased from forty-eight to seventy-five years between 1900 and 1990, an improvement of twenty-seven years.[1] However, if a man achieved age forty-five, his life expectancy over the same period increased from twenty-four to thirty-one years, an improvement of *only* seven years. Much of the improvements in life expectancy over the twentieth century resulted from less mortality at younger ages. For example, a variety of improvements in public health dramatically reduced pediatric mortality in the last century, resulting in prolongation of life expectancy. The infant who survives the first year of life and lives to old age increases life expectancy much more than ten eighty-year-old people who live to age eighty-five. Mortality in children is now very low, and therefore there is little room for life expectancy gains from further improvements in pediatric care. This fact is regularly debated in newborn intensive care units, where costs dramatically increase for very small reductions in neonatal (i.e., newborn) mortality. Somehow the chronic pulmonary, visual, and neurologic morbidity (or disease results) associated with saving extremely premature neonates is not considered when evaluating costs.

Mortality by Disease

The outstanding report of Thomas Peery thirty years ago provides an excellent and informative assessment of the diseases contributing to mortality over the past century. [2] The reader will quickly recognize that chronologically Dr. Peery's graphs (Figures 1 and 2) end at 1970. Despite being a few years out-of-date, these charts so very clearly illustrate basic points. The several lines depicted on the graphs become horizontal in 1950. As we will discuss in chapter 3, John Bailar demon-

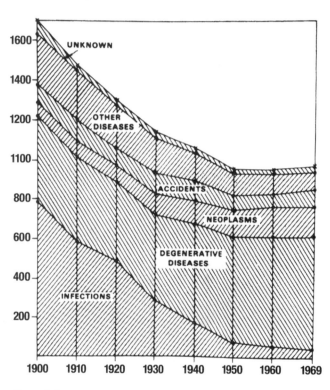

Figure 1. Representation of death rates per 100,000 people in the United States from all causes, 1900 to 1969. Reprinted with permission from the *American Journal of Clinical Pathology 1975*; 63: 458.

strates clearly that both the incidence and mortality of cancer has remained unchanged for over thirty years. Similarly, mortality from infectious disease, which prior to 1950 was mainly in children, has leveled out to a minimum in 1970 and can go no lower. I therefore conclude that the graphs provide critical information applicable today, despite being thirty years old. Total mortality (Figure 1) in 1900 was one thousand seven hundred per one hundred thousand people and declined to nine hundred fifty in 1970. Note that almost half (eight hundred) of all deaths were due to infectious disease in 1900, declining to about seventy-five in 1970, with a further slight decline since. This is because the very young were no longer dying of infections, and adults were dying from so-called degenerative diseases of aging. Cancer (i.e., neoplasm) deaths increased moderately over the century, a fact related to increased life expectancy; cancer is predominately a disease of older persons.

A more specific breakdown (Figure 2) of the types of infections causing mortality over the same period reveals a dramatic decline in deaths due to intestinal infections. Note that tuberculosis mortality almost completely disappeared in the United States in the first half of the century, declining from two hundred deaths to virtually none by the end of the twentieth century. The virtual disappearance of tuberculosis mortality antedated the availability of anti-tuberculous chemotherapy. The improvement was due to better iso-

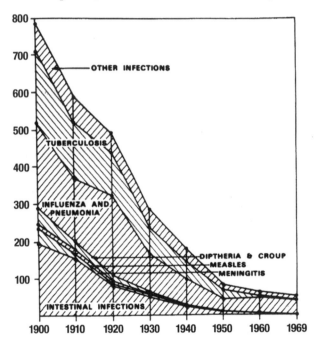

Figure 2. Death rates from infectious disease, United States, 1900 to 1969, by major types. Reprinted with permission from the *American Journal of Clinical Pathology 1975*; 63: 459.

lation, nutrition, etc. Influenza and pneumonia remain significant causes of death, particularly in the aged. A very common misconception relates the decline of infectious disease mortality to the introduction of antibiotics during and shortly after World War II. However, a closer perusal of both Figures would clearly indicate that most of the mortality decline, possibly 80 or more percent, occurred prior to the introduction of antibiotics. Most of the decline was due to improvements in public health, specifically in safe drinking water, better sewage disposal, improved nutrition, higher living standards, selected immunizations, and lower birth rates. Direct patient care by physicians had relatively little impact on the dramatic decline of infectious disease mortality.

FACTORS INFLUENCING LIFE EXPECTANCY

Gender

We have been accustomed to seeing women live longer than men in most of the Western democracies. Although women live almost six years longer than do men, this gap in life expectancy is decreasing. In the last decade of the 1900s, male life expectancy went up 1.9 years, substantially higher than the 0.6 year gain for women. The quoted reason is that the reduction in cigarette smoking accounted for much of the male improvement. Perhaps if women were as successful as men in quitting smoking, the gap might reverse.

Surprisingly, the life expectancy gap between men and women is of relatively recent origin. Until about 150 years ago, women's life expectancy was shorter than or identical to that of men. Although much debated, the change may relate to the decline of mortality due to childbirth fever (i.e., puerperal sepsis) and changes in the organization of society causing less lethal risks to women.

The highest life expectancies at birth are now reported among Japanese women and Americans in the Upper Midwest; the Dakotas, Minnesota and Iowa are on top. These high levels of life expectancy may be socio-economic in origin in both Japan and the Upper Midwest.

National Origin

Japan and Chad (West Africa) represent the extremes of life expectancy in the world; life expectancy is seventy-eight years in Japan and thirty-six years in Chad. To a great extent, life expectancies in the Western democracies and the Pacific Rim nations are high and about equal. The poverty, social disruptions, and political turmoil in the Third World nations undoubtedly contribute to reduced life expectancy. Since the decline of the Soviet Union, life expectancy in Russia has lowered further, likely related to social factors such as heavy smoking and vodka consumption.

Diet

Despite abundant concern in the United States about the quantity of saturated fats in the diet and its role in cardiovascular disorders, it is difficult to incriminate diet as a major factor in life expectancy. For example, up until recent years, Japanese consumed a diet low in saturated fats, whereas people in Switzerland and Austria had high fat diets.[3] Despite the dietary differences, all three nations have similar longevity. Perhaps adequate caloric intake may impact longevity more than does consumption of saturated fats. The role of the current epidemic of obesity in the Western world may adversely affect life expectancy. The data is not yet adequate to evaluate this possibility.

Socio-Economic Factors

These factors are quite diverse, and yet, the contribution of these factors to the variations in life expectancy is obvious. Very little impact on longevity can be attributed to moral issues, unless morality influences lifestyles. For example, whereas in socially liberal Sweden, 50 percent of births involve unmarried women, in more conservative Japan, less than 1 percent of births are to single women. Life expectancies in both nations are the same. However, a disparity of life expectancies has been documented in a comparison of Utah and Nevada in the United States. Mormon Utah, whose people generally do not smoke and drink and live rather conservative lives, has very extended life expectancy. On the other hand, Nevada, where people adopt obviously different social life-styles, has a much lower life expectancy.

Income and education levels clearly affect life expectancy. More affluent and more educated people live longer. Fertility rates, higher in the poor and less educated, are associated with shorter lives. Education and resulting lowered birth rates may be the greatest factor in increasing longevity.

Cigarette smoking is a major factor contributing to premature mortality. The United States experiences 450,000 excess deaths annually as a direct result of smoking. Since smoking is more prevalent in those with lower income and education, smoking may be a major part of this socio-economic disparity. Obesity is also more prevalent in the lower socio-economic classes of society, possibly also contributing to the longevity disparity.

Inheritance

The value of having long-lived parents to an individual's life expectancy has long been debated.[4] The mapping of the human genome has not identified a single gene or group of genes responsible for one's life expectancy. It is clear that long-lived parents have children who live longer. Conversely, parents who die young have offspring whose lives are shortened.

What is the secret to living a long life? Remain in good health, be employed, don't smoke cigarettes, be female, have normal weight, and, of course, select long-lived parents.

LIFE SPAN

Whereas life expectancy is a readily calculated parameter, life span remains a controversial, subjective, and theoretical concept. We sorely need a distinction between life expectancy and life span. Most people believe that the two concepts are identical. They are not. A small group of epidemiologists have championed the concept of a finite life span.

This small group appears willing to do so despite the fact that the concept is inherently pessimistic, and so is opposed to the American trend of unbridled optimism.

We tend to accept the idea that, with sufficient expenditure of resources and energy, American medicine will continue its progress toward wiping out human disease and increasing life expectancy without limit. This view manifested several decades ago during the presidency of Lyndon Johnson. Michael Debakey of Baylor University, a friend of Johnson, proposed *Heart, Stroke and Cancer*, a program designed to wipe out these three major diseases in a short time. At least forty years have elapsed since this program began, and these diseases are still with us.

Those emphasizing the concept of a finite life span argue that humans are programmed to live a certain number of years. No matter the advances in medical science, life expectancy will not exceed the programmed life span. Several arguments support their position.

Researchers have disproved the longevity claims coming from the Russian Caucasus and Greece. [5] Both nations have claimed life expectancies as high as 130-140 years. The Russian claims probably date from early in World War I, when the Kaiser's German army on the Eastern front was destroying the Czar's armies. Rather than put their lives at risk in the military, many young Russian men claimed advanced age, thereby exempting themselves from conscription. When Russia withdrew from the war, these "older" citizens retained their claim to advanced years, thereby supporting the claim of extreme age. However, baptismal and other documents revealed the true ages of these very old Russians. A similar distortion of age occurred in Greece, a nation noted for its veneration of elders. In order to be venerated, a significant number of Greeks claimed advanced age when they were middle-aged, thereby "achieving" an age beyond their natural one. It is now believed that the maximum achievable age of humans is somewhere around 120 years. This nation recently lost one or two very old people below the age of 120 due to natural causes. These people were relatives of Civil War soldiers.

Also supporting the thesis that people live a finite life span is the fact that the number of centenarians (people over the age of one hundred) per capita has remained constant. Although we casually assume that there are more very old people alive than ever before, the number of centenarians per one hundred thousand people is unchanged. Many of our Founding Fathers achieved advanced age, despite of, or because of, the absence of scientific medicine. For example, John Adams lived to ninety-three; Thomas Jefferson was riding a horse until he was about eighty-two; George Washington, our first president, died at sixty-seven, probably due to medical care. George had peritonsillar abscess (i.e., quinsy), the treatment of which at that time was phlebotomy (or blood-letting). The doctors actually bled George to death. He might have lived on for many more years at Mount Vernon had he not been compromised by medical care. I recently lost a good friend at 104 years of age, who was practicing his classical violin until a week before he died.

Finally, the work of Hayflick and associates with tissue cultures of human fibroblasts supports the concept of a finite life span.[6] Fibroblasts are the normal body cells that make connective tissue. In these tissue cultures, after about forty cell divisions and despite appearing histologically "normal," the fibroblasts ceased multiplying and died. The presumption is that living organisms are genetically programmed to live a defined interval of time. The proponents of a finite life span have put a number on their belief.[7] The average life span should be about eighty-five years. Two standard deviations above and below the average age indicate that 95 percent of persons will die between seventy-five and ninety-five years. If we accept an average life span of eighty-five years, some groups of people, notably Japanese women and North Dakotans, have life expectancies currently very close to the theoretical life span. Improving life expectancy in these favored groups would require undue amounts of revenue and energy, apparently for very little yield. Some groups in our society have an inordinate number of deaths due to self-destructive violence. These deaths are sociologic in origin and not amenable to correction by medical care.

LIMITS OF MEDICINE

How do the concepts of life expectancy and the theoretic life span illuminate the extent to which medicine should go in its attempt to wipe out illness in the truly aged. We have already approached the limits of reducing mortality in young patients. Further attempts at saving the lives of extremely premature neonates (i.e., newborns) can only increase chronic neurologic and pulmonary disability. These infants will have lives of infirmity, dependence, and early death. If all cancers were eliminated as a cause of death, life expectancy would increase only 2.3 years, but at phenomenal cost. With this small improvement in mind, one can not help but wonder about the yield of modern oncology chemotherapy in treating recurrent cancers, most of which are eventually fatal.

One controversial concept is that suggested by the theory of competing risks.[8] This theory clearly defines the limits of medicine. It addresses particularly aging people in whom life expectancy is already limited. Expressed simply, the theory states that if one is already eighty years old, and one's doctor "cures" one of one ailment, one will likely die of another quite soon. People of advancing years usually die of cancer or cardiovascular disease. In this age group, assuming that a cancer is "cured," the patient will soon succumb to heart disease. Curing disease in old people only changes the cause of death, not the duration of life. Evidence to support this "theory" is available from the Framingham study, a magnificent long-term documentation of the causes of death over the last forty or fifty years. As deaths due to hypertensive and cardiovascular disease declined over the past few decades, mortality from colon cancer correspondingly increased. In other words, only the cause of death was changed, not the life expectancy.

Many pathologists, especially those who practiced in an earlier era when autopsies were commonly performed, have first-hand knowledge of the causes of death in the aged. Although autopsies on nonagenarians (ninety-year-old people) and centenarians were quite rare, those that were performed were characterized by the lack of pathologic findings. We often had no findings to explain an old person's death. We believed the deaths to be due to a natural senescence occurring in old people, at which point the tiniest insults to health, which would ordinarily be of no consequence to younger people, could be sufficient to cause death. If biologic senescence and the theory of competing risks are true, then our attempts to conquer disease in old patients yield neither longevity nor quality of life. We only postpone the inevitable.

Another more philosophical question, one also almost too sensitive for our society to address, is the gain medical science might achieve by increasing life expectancy to the theoretical maximum life span. Won't we create a population of the very old who are frail, senile, dependent, and living in nursing homes or assisted care facilities? Is this what we want, or should we be satisfied with a few less years of life that are vital, fulfilling, and independent? Those posing these questions unfortunately take great risks and abuse from elements of our society, such as pro-life groups or individuals, who consider life at any cost the paramount concern. The latter apparently would be comfortable with the population in Jonathan Swift's *Gulliver's Travels*, in which Gulliver visited Struldbrugs (who were immortal). These unfortunate people continued to age, becoming more infirm and unwell, but never died. I doubt that this is an eventuality we prefer.

SUMMARY

Although the concept of life expectancy and lifespan are rarely considered in everyday medical practice, taking them and their implications for the limits of medicine into account is the sole way to rein in inflating health costs. The current frightening increase in healthcare costs derives entirely from the lack of cost-benefit considerations in modern medical care. Americans believe optimistically that, if we expend more resources on medical care and research, the health of the citizens will improve commensurately. In other words, there should be no financial constraint on how much we spend on medical care expenses. Unfortunately, this view ignores the limits of what medical care can offer; this lack of consideration increases directly healthcare cost inflation.

The greatest improvements in medical care concern the control of infectious diseases. Although many credit the improvements to the use of antibiotics, most of the improvement occurred prior to the availability of antibiotics. Improvements in public health, not medical care, are primarily responsible for the dramatic reduction in infectious disease mortality.

The concept of a finite lifespan, in which the average achievable age of Americans would be eighty-five years, is inherently pessimistic. Assuming that a finite lifespan is a reality, some of the populations in the Western world are quite close to that age. Therefore, further efforts to prolong life expectancy will be very difficult to attain, and of course will entail large costs for little yield in quality of health or longevity.

The several factors influencing life expectancy resist medical care improvement. Major factors are economic and social, and are unrelated to what medical care can offer. Further contributing to the inability of healthcare to influence longevity is the "theory of competing risks." As one approaches the theoretical lifespan, one's longevity becomes limited by multiple health problems. The aged person must die of something. Curing the elderly person of one disorder does not immunize him or her against another fatal condition. Only the cause of death is changed; life expectancy is not increased.

References

1. *Statistical Bulletin* (1991 July – September): 19-25.

2. T. M. Peery, *"The New and Old Diseases: A Study of Mortality Trends in the United States, 1900 – 1969," Am J Clin Path* 63 (1975): 453-74.

3. T. J., Moore, *Lifespan: Who Lives Longer and Why.* (New York: Simon and Schuster, 1993), 73.

4. M. R. Hawkins, *"Inheritance and longevity," Bull Johns Hopkins Hosp* 117: (1965) 24.

5. S. H. Preston, *Biological and Social Aspects and the Length of Life.* (Liege, Belgium: Ordina Editions, 1980), 443-5.

6. L. Hayflick, *"The Cell Biology of Human Aging," Sci Am* 242 (1980): 58-65.

7. J. F. Fries, *"Aging, Natural Death, and the Compression of Morbidity," NEJM* 303, No. 3 (1980): 130-5.

8. J. v Maloney, *"The Limits of Medicine," Ann Surg* 194 (1981): 247-55.

2

Infectious Diseases

Infectious disease is far too large a topic to cover in one chapter. As we indicated in the first chapter, dramatic progress has been made against infectious disease mortality since the twentieth century, at least in the developed world. During this time, infectious disease mortality in the United States has declined by almost 90 percent. Most of the decline occurred prior to the introduction of antibiotics, despite widespread belief to the contrary. Although the value of antibiotics in combatting individual patient infections cannot be questioned, public health improvement played a far greater role in the decline in morbidity (i.e., disease effect) and mortality of the population. In recent times, the excessive use of antimicrobial drugs has created new problems, the extent of which will be discussed later. The introduction of antibiotics during and immediately after World War II led to unfortunate misconceptions about their function and value. In fact, the Surgeon General in 1969 said, "The war on infectious disease has been won." How wrong he was.

Because of space limitations, we will cover only the most compelling aspects of the history of infectious diseases. Much of the history can only be estimated because the science of microbiology is only slightly more than one hundred years old. As history attests, a great deal of the control of infectious disease occurred without the benefit of bacteriology and virology. It is widely accepted that infectious diseases have played a much greater role in the history of humankind than have wars, starvation, political disruptions, and the like. Up until World War II, many more soldiers died of wound infections than direct battle trauma. Major advances in the handling of battle wounds were developed during World War II, resulting in dramatic improvements in outcomes for wounded soldiers. The handling of battle wounds as depicted so graphically in the television series M*A*S*H correctly showed that the chances of survival for a wounded soldier reaching an aid station alive were excellent. Even simply packing traumatic wounds open, instead of closing them, was a major advance in the prevention of fatal wound infections.

HISTORY OF INFECTIOUS DISEASES

The Plague

During the past two millennia, the infectious disease known as the plague played a huge role in the history of humankind. The staggering numbers of people infected and who died of the disease significantly affected the economies of all nations of Western Europe. As many as one-third of the population of a country would die in a short period of time, creating major labor shortages and adversely affecting the economy. At times, the disposal of bodies was a major logistical problem.

There are two basic types of plague infection, bubonic and pulmonic. Both were equally lethal, but bubonic plague was far more common. The contagious elements of each were identical; only clinical manifestations differed. The Justinian plague of the sixth century, named after a Pope, began in the Middle East and Turkey, and then rampaged through Western Europe, killing as many as one-third of the population. The second major plague also appears to have been Mideast in origin, and it, too, caused major problems in Western Europe, this time during the fourteenth century. The plague and the Crusades overlapped, and this period is particularly well-described in the historical novel, A Distant Mirror, by Barbara Tuchman.[1] Subsequent but less major plagues occurred in India and China in the nineteenth and twentieth centuries, respectively.

If these plague epidemics had occurred in the current world, with its population of 6.5 billion people, and with the close contacts created by air and other kinds of travel, the number of fatalities would be too high to comprehend. Civilization would either be destroyed or set back for generations. If extrapolation from the early plague epidemics is feasible, the fatalities might be akin to those from a nuclear holocaust.

Elements of the Plague

The disease is created by the interrelation of a host, a transmitting agent, and a specific bacterium.[2] The primary hosts are rodents, most commonly the ubiquitous house rat. Humans are accidental hosts; the flea prefers biting rodents. The infected flea suffers from bowel obstruction caused by the proliferation of the causative bacterium, *Yersinia pestis*, and starves. Before it dies of starvation, however, it bites another host, thereby transmitting the bacteria. The house rat is unusually susceptible to the infection; during the epidemic, almost all house rats die. When the flea bites a human, strictly as a secondary host, the human becomes infected. The majority of infected humans, well over 50 percent, die of the plague.

Congested life in cities, where close proximity of rats, fleas and humans exists, contributes to the extent of the epidemic. Some of the rich and powerful people in Europe recognized that most cases occurred in large cities with congested populations of very poor people. Those who could, moved to the countryside to avoid the plague; many succeeded and the epidemic gradually burned out. This basic concept of the contagion of infectious disease was understood, despite the complete lack of bacteriology or any element of what we'd call scientific medicine.

What made the plague so frightening was the almost complete lack of ability to treat or avoid it, with the small exception of abandoning the congested cities by those who could afford to. The epidemic struck anyone and everyone; it completely lacked discrimination and was beyond anyone's control. In this respect, the plague epidemics of bygone eras were completely different than the current AIDS (acquired immune deficiency syndrome) epidemic caused by HIV (human immunodeficiency virus). The AIDS epidemic is completely defined, as we know the causative microorganism and the means of transmission, and have some semblance of effective therapy. Despite the state of knowledge of AIDS, however, the epidemic continues unabated.

Looking back on the major plague epidemics, we might wonder if history will repeat itself. After all, the three elements still exist. We certainly have not eliminated the causative flea, the house rat, or *Yersinia pestis*. The sole change is that we now have several antibiotics capable of killing the organism. In fact, isolated cases continue to occur, particularly in the southwest part of the United States. The infection appears to remain contained to a few areas with unique climatic conditions. The ability to recognize and control the infection may mean that future epidemics of plague will not occur.

AIDS

As indicated above, the absence of medical science during the plague epidemics does not apply to the current situation involving AIDS. Following the observation[3] of a rare form of pneumonia occurring in homosexual young men in New York City in 1981, scientists in the United States and France simultaneously identified the causative virus, HIV, in 1983. The current epidemic is uniquely well studied, and yet control of the epidemic appears extremely difficult, if not impossible. In the United States and Western Europe, transmission of the virus is largely facilitated by male homosexual practices and illicit intravenous drug use. Females are less likely to be infected, unless they have sex with bisexual males or intravenous drug users. Africa presents a far more ominous picture, with infection rates extremely high and transmission control almost impossible. In Africa, AIDS is largely a heterosexual disease, involving men and women equally, and is facilitated by the sexual promiscuity dependent on migrant employment opportunities. Jobs to support a family are scarce so that men migrate for extended periods to other nations or localities. The young workers consort with the almost universally infected prostitutes, thereby bringing the infection home to unsuspecting wives. As most cases occur in young people and parents of small children, the tragedy of AIDS in Africa is even worse.

Although anti-viral therapy is reasonably effective in treating AIDS, modifying the clinical course and delaying mortality, HIV effectively hides in the body and may recur at any time. Further, HIV exhibits antigenic drift, changing its identity regularly, so that therapy becomes less effective with time. Episodic or incomplete therapy facilitates resistance to anti-viral drugs. The problems that inhibit development of a vaccine are similar to those of developing vaccines for our influenza epidemics. Because of this, and because therapy is only partially effective and immunization is compromised by HIV antigenic changes, control of transmission of the virus appears to be the most fruitful direction to take. Unfortunately, transmission is directly related to sociological practices least amenable to change. Compounding the difficulty of controlling the spread of HIV is the false sense of security amongst the groups of people most likely to be involved. Many young male homosexuals mistakenly believe that safe sex is now unimportant. That is, many believe that if one becomes infected through unsafe sex, one's infection will be treated effectively. This frightening attitude is a regrettable consequence of the development of more effective therapy.

Influenza

Although influenza afflicted humankind prior to the twentieth century, the international pandemic of the Spanish flu at the end of World War I is the most clearly documented and was by far the most devastating.[4] Although virology was not sufficiently advanced at the time, we have serologic evidence of the epidemic from survivors or stored blood serum. In fact, the epidemic was thought to be bacterial in origin; hence the name *Haemophilus influenza*. In the few months from 1918 through 1919, as many as one hundred million people worldwide died of the flu. Considering that the world population at the time was only slightly more than one billion people, as contrasted to the current figure of six billion, puts this into perspective.

Such flus pose significant problems. In addition to population crowding, travel from one place to another is now greatly facilitated by airplanes, and the flu spreads easily and quickly under such conditions. Despite the availability of potent antibiotics, influenza is a viral infection, for which anti-viral drugs are limited in effectiveness. Furthermore and most significantly, the main problem with control of influenza is antigenic drift, a process of mutation in the virus each year, so that people require repeated immunizations reflecting the changes. The recent vaccine production episode in England exemplifies the problem. A major vaccine producer discovered significant bacterial contamination in several vaccine batches. This technical misadventure mandated a halt to that plant's production, resulting in a major vaccine shortage for that year. Fortunately, however, the subsequent season was relatively mild. There is no guarantee, however, that the virus will not mutate to the more virulent form that existed in 1918-19, spawning an epidemic with very high mortality, possibly causing hundreds of millions of deaths.

The surface proteins of the influenza virus are responsible for contagion and pathogenicity (i.e., the disease-causing potential), and also are subject to mutation change (i.e., the antigenic drift). The problem of antigenic drift contributes to the difficulty in immunizing non-immune populations. Because of our lack of prior exposure to new antigens, major antigenic drift could be responsible for a major epidemic and very high mortality. Compounding the problem in the Spanish flu epidemic of 1918-19 was the infection's predilection to affect young people in their twenties and thirties, the most productive years of their lives. This pathogenicity also involved rapid illness and death. Large numbers of soldiers in the process of military discharge at the end of World War I died in numbers approximating combat deaths. Additional major epidemics occurred in 1957 and 1968, causing some observers to postulate a ten-year periodicity. Each of these epidemics originated in the Far East, thus the names Asian or Hong Kong flu.

The current legitimate public health concern is avian flu, which originated primarily in fowl in China. Millions of chickens have been destroyed in an attempt to control the spread of this new influenza virus. That the avian flu can involve humans is no longer debated. Workers exposed in the chicken raising industry have become infected; around one hundred cases have been reported with high mortality. If antigenic drift occurs, enabling the virus to achieve person-to-person spread, a serious flu epidemic is possible. Since immunization against this new virus is unavailable, a potential flu disaster could arrive on the world scene.

Measles and Smallpox

Smallpox and measles played a role in the colonization of America. Previously, both viral infections were non-existent in the Western Hemisphere. Spanish explorers and conquerors brought the diseases with them, with devastating consequences to native populations completely lacking in any immunity. The Aztec and Inca civilizations were almost completely destroyed by a small number of invading Spaniards. North America Indians were probably also decimated by these viral infections.

Although Edward Jenner, a nineteenth century English physician, is credited with the discovery of smallpox vaccination, less effective immunization techniques were available at least one hundred years earlier.[5] George Washington's Continental Army was inoculated with samples taken from active smallpox lesions, creating significant immunity, but also causing smallpox itself. Jenner's work stemmed from his observation that milkmaids had smooth complexions, in stark contrast to the pockmarked skin disfiguring the faces of many women who had survived the infection. The milkmaids had contracted vaccinia, a related bovine (i.e., cattle) infection, which provided them with immunity to the more severe smallpox infection. The attenuated (i.e., less pathogenic) vaccinia infection was mild and short-lived, but conveyed immunity.

Smallpox has been eradicated from the world, which is a tremendous accomplishment of the World Health Organization.[6] The last cases were tracked down in parts of East Africa (in Somalia) some twenty-five years ago; no new cases have occurred since. Smallpox was amenable to extinction because of several factors intrinsic to the virus. The virus is limited to humans; no animal reservoir exists. Infected humans either die of the disease or survive with lifelong immunity; survivors do not harbor the virus. Finally, the disease can be reliably prevented by vaccination; lifelong immunity occurs. The sole remaining concern about smallpox is its use in terrorism. Frozen batches of the virus are stored in

Moscow and Atlanta. If terrorists were to obtain these stored supplies, the possibilities of terrorist action using the virus would be devastating since many people have never received immunization, given its absence as an active disease.

OTHER HISTORICALLY SIGNIFICANT INFECTIONS

Yellow Fever

The Panama Canal would never have been constructed had yellow fever not been controlled. Dr. Walter Reed, a military physician, was assigned to do research on yellow fever. He learned, despite the absence of the science of virology, that mosquitoes multiplying in standing water, such as that in the area of the proposed canal, transmitted the infection. The Panama Canal was not the only place supporting yellow fever. Large areas of the United States, including states and cities as far north as Philadelphia, Pennsylvania, had many cases of yellow fever during the period of the canal's construction. Mosquito-born infections in the United States predominantly represent several varieties of encephalitis (i.e., brain viral infections). However, most problems with mosquitoes are simply nuisance factors, rather than causes of disease.

Tuberculosis

Some Egyptian mummies show the ravages of tuberculosis. All civilizations have had to contend with this chronic and often fatal bacterial infection. There are estimates that half of all causes of death in England during the seventeenth century were due to tuberculosis. Tuberculosis also played a role in the English monarchy. Edward VI, the sole living son of Jane Seymour, Henry VIII's third wife, died at age six of a disease experts believe was tuberculosis. He was sickly for years, coughed a lot, was emaciated (hence the former term "consumption") and died as a youth. Because Henry had no surviving male heir, the daughter of Henry's second wife, Anne Boleyn, became Elizabeth I, Queen of England. She ruled long and well, and is credited with the rise of the British Empire and Britain's resultant industrial power.

The management of tuberculosis has dramatically changed through the twentieth century. It was widely believed that fresh air and sunshine were required to heal the infection. This belief was depicted in the literary work, *Magic Mountain*, by Thomas Mann.[7] In the early half of the twentieth century, collapse therapy was the vogue, in which the infected portions of the lung were "rested" by collapsing adjacent portions of the lungs. When streptomycin and isoniazid were introduced after World War II, anti-tuberculous chemotherapy dramatically changed the direction of therapy. No longer was isolation required. Infected individuals could go about their lives, as long as they took their medicines. It is now believed that the only therapy that historically made any difference, prior to chemotherapy, was isolation in tuberculosis sanitoria. Isolation prevented spread to non-infected individuals. Until anti-tuberculosis chemotherapy was available, people got well or did poorly simply as a matter of luck and induced immunity. Collapse therapy probably did nothing except keep phthisiologists (i.e., tuberculosis physicians) busy.

The Control of Childbirth Fever (Puerperal Sepsis)

The one physician given almost the entire credit for control of childbirth fever is Ignaz Semmelweis, a Hungarian obstetrician working in Vienna and Budapest in the middle of the nineteenth century; other physicians were somewhat involved.[8] Ignaz actually worked himself to death trying to teach his fellow physicians the simple hygienic measures capable of preventing the infection. Keep in mind that the science of bacteriology was unknown in his time, making understanding this infectious disease infinitely difficult. In addition to the absence of the science of bacteriology, Ignaz's major problem was dealing with an entrenched medical bureaucracy that feared and thwarted medical science.

Ignaz went to medical school in Vienna. The major hospital and teaching facility was the Algemeine Krankenhaus (i.e., the general hospital), a part of which housed the Vienna Lying-In (or obstetrics) Hospital, where Ignaz trained and worked. The Lying-In Hospital ostensibly served to provide a maternity facility for the poor and downtrodden of society who could not afford private care, and also a training site for obstetricians. Many of the problems that Ignaz had with the German physicians of Vienna were of his own making. His personality did not allow for compromise or diplomacy. He fought with the hidebound, conservative, and truly ignorant medical establishment. Perhaps if he had been less pugnacious and more willing to compromise, he might have seen the fruits of his life work.

The First Division of the Lying-In Hospital was the training site for the education of new physicians and undergraduate medical students. The Second Division was created to teach midwives, with the faculty composed of both physicians and senior midwives. The two divisions were of equal physical size and patient complement. To maintain this equality, admitted patients were alternately assigned to either division. For reasons I will explain later, many patients developed a preference for the Second Division and, in fact, occasionally manipulated the admissions system to be admitted to the midwives' division.

When Ignaz completed his obstetrics training, he received a staff position in the First Division as a subordinate to Professor Klein. He immediately learned that deaths from childbirth fever (or puerperal sepsis) were extremely common at the Lying-In Hospital, something that didn't occur as frequently to the women who delivered babies at home under private care. Ignaz began examining the mortality experience of both divisions, and quickly learned that lethal puerperal sepsis was three to five times as common in the First Division (where physicians and medical students trained). This fact was also known in Vienna medical circles, but no one but Ignaz questioned the finding. He was indeed pugnacious and inquisitive. Incidentally, similar mortality from puerperal sepsis existed at the Lying-In Hospitals throughout Europe; the Viennese experience was neither unique nor worse than elsewhere.

When Ignaz questioned others about the reasons for the excessive mortality from puerperal sepsis, he learned very little. Some thought it was due to "cosmic-telluric influences," a phenomenon involving the environment in some unknown way. Others suggested fetid air and patient crowding. This made no sense to Ignaz, because both divisions were of similar size and both buildings were immediately adjacent, subject to the same flow of air. The ringing of the priests' bells after patients' deaths was considered. The priests were prevailed upon to cease ringing the bells; mortality was unchanged. Foreign medical students with strange languages and coarse demeanors were incriminated. Many were discharged; the mortality remained the same. Ignaz became increasingly depressed and agitated, because he had no answers.

He observed that women who delivered before arriving at the Lying-In Hospital had a very low incidence of puerperal sepsis. This fact was obvious to the poor and uneducated women patients, and they did what they could to avoid the First Division. This group of poverty-stricken and unsophisticated women had greater insight into the disease problem than the haughty and imperious physicians of Vienna.

Ignaz's mental state deteriorated and he went on vacation for a month. When he returned, the situation was no better, and to his further discomfort, he learned that his autopsy associate and friend, Dr. Koletchka, had died. An autopsy had fortunately been performed and Ignaz found the autopsy report amazing. Death was due to widespread sepsis (i.e., disseminated infection), which had apparently started from an insignificant finger cut sustained during the performance of an autopsy on a patient who had died from puerperal sepsis.

The pathologic findings were identical to those of most young women who died from puerperal sepsis, except for some important differences. Dr. Koletchka was a man, did not have a uterus, and had not recently delivered a baby. Ignaz was astounded. His friend had died from a disease obviously derived from and related to an autopsy done on a woman with puerperal sepsis. From his experience performing autopsies and practicing obstetrics in the labor room and delivery suite, Ignaz knew that something—he called it cadaveric principle—was carried on the hands of students and physicians from the morgue to the obstetric area. The daily hospital routine involved performing autopsies in the morning and working in the obstetrics area the remainder of the day. Basic cleanliness wasn't observed; gloves were unavailable and handwashing was a rare occurrence.

Ignaz deduced that the physicians themselves were responsible for the deaths due to puerperal sepsis. This was unacceptable to most physicians, and, to a point, was rejected. Nevertheless, Ignaz instituted hand-washing and rinsing in a chlorinated lime (a disinfectant) solution following the performance of an autopsy and between patient obstetrics examinations. Immediately, the incidence of puerperal sepsis and mortality plummeted, and Ignaz was for a time happy and respected. Unfortunately, Professor Klein was neither happy nor tolerant. Ignaz was discharged and returned to his native Budapest to continue his obstetric practice. His antiseptic teaching bore limited fruit in Hungary. His followers were few and were not in organized medicine. Physicians generally refused to accept his teachings. His mental state further deteriorated.

When it became obvious to family and friends that Ignaz was on the verge of psychosis, he was scheduled to be admitted to the psychiatric pavilion of the Algemeine Krankenhaus in Vienna. He allegedly visited the morgue at the Lying-In Hospital, where puerperal sepsis had returned because his teachings had been rejected. He thrust his hand into the infected pelvis of a young woman recently dead of puerperal sepsis, and intentionally lacerated his fingers. Within two weeks after admission to the psychiatric hospital, Ignaz died of sepsis in the same manner as his friend, Dr. Koletchka.

Ignaz's teachings did not die, however. By 1890, sterile obstetric technique was introduced throughout the Western world; puerperal sepsis is now a rare occurrence. While other investigators had considered the contagious aspects of puerperal sepsis before Ignaz and had recommended cleanliness in obstetrics care, none had had the perseverance to take on the medical community. They were therefore less effective. Ignaz was truly a medical hero, personally responsible for saving the lives of millions of young women and their newborn infants.

ANTIBIOTICS

The use and abuse of antibiotics plays an important role in the history of infectious disease. When Florey accidentally discovered penicillin prior to World War II, this new "wonder drug" achieved some spectacular results in treating serious wound infections in injured soldiers. Following its introduction into civilian use when World War II ended, its impressive value was soon added to by discovery of additional antibiotics with a broader spectrum of antibacterial activity. Quite soon thereafter, resistant forms of staphylococci emerged, and resistant strains increased to the point that most pathogenic staphylococci exhibit complete resistance to penicillin. Resistance to virtually every antibiotic has gradually developed in many organisms, so that serious hospital infections are now occasionally untreatable.

There are several causes of the developing antibiotic resistance. Strains with inherent antibiotic resistance are intrinsic to populations of bacteria. When antibiotics are administered, the susceptible strains are either killed or inhibited, permitting the inherently resistant germs to multiply. It is exquisitely clear that excessive administration of antibiotics contributes to the emergence of resistance. When a particular antibiotic is no longer used, the resistance quickly diminishes, enabling resumption of the use of that antibiotic, hopefully with some discrimination.

Many explanations have been put forth to explain the excessive use of antibiotics. Simple ignorance may be the prime factor. Instead of deciding whether an infection is due to a virus or a bacterium, physicians prescribe antibiotics "just in case." Other usage is designed to prevent bacterial superimposition, a phenomenon generally absent in most documented studies. Some physicians succumb to parental or school pressures, which is often the mistaken belief that a respiratory infection can be shortened or improved by antibiotic therapy. There are other similar reasons, none convincing. As one very smart person once stated, "Although man can produce a better mousetrap, nature always seems to build a better mouse."

Antibiotics and Neoplasms

Historically, infectious diseases and cancers were considered distinct. Cancer was considered an error of mutation in body cells caused by environmental factors. Infections were considered caused by discrete microorganisms. Modern bacteria are specific plant species and viruses are incomplete parts of cells. Given this, infections and cancers were completely separate entities in medical thinking. Over the past few decades, however, certain microorganisms, either bacteria or viruses, have been etiologically (i.e., as a cause) related to specific tumors, demonstrating that cancers can be caused by infectious agents.

Tumor Examples

Nasopharyngeal carcinoma has been associated with Epstein-Barr virus (EBV) for decades. In fact, this cancer, rare in the United States and Europe but very common in China and Hong Kong, is caused by EBV. Carcinoma of the uterine cervix is now etiologically related to at least two strains of human papillomavirus (HPV), an organism transmitted to women during sexual intercourse. Immunization against the HPV strains is now being developed; hopefully, this serious cancer can be prevented. Tumors of the stomach, both lymphomas and certain mucosal cancers, are now associated with infection with *Helicobacter pylori*.[9] The latter was first incriminated with chronic gastritis and peptic ulcers of the stomach and duodenum. We now can treat and cure lymphomas of the stomach with the same antibiotics used to treat acid-peptic disease of the stomach and duodenum. Other relationships between microorganisms and neoplasms are now being studied.

SUMMARY

Infectious diseases have had major impact on the history of humankind. Although antibiotics have had a major contribution to improved therapy of individual patient infections, the major contributions to the decline of infectious disease mortality have been improved public health measures. The use of antibiotics has been a two-edged sword. Although very useful in treating specific infections in individual patients, excessive antibiotic prescribing and use has contributed to antibiotic resistance with many bacteria, creating serious patient care problems. Infectious diseases will always be with us. Their role in causing cancer is now being studied intensively.

References

1. B. W. Tuchman, *A Distant Mirror: The Calamitous 14th Century* (New York: Alfred A. Knopf, 1978).

2. G. Cravens and J. S. Marr, *The Black Death* (New York: Ballantine Books, 1977).

3. J. L. Jacobs, D. M. Libby, R. A. Winters, et al., "A Cluster of Pneumocystic Pneumonia in Adults Without Predisposing Illnesses," *NEJM*, 324 (1991): 245-50.

4. W. H. Barker and J. P. Mullooly, "Pneumonia and Influenza Deaths During Epidemics," *Arch Int Med* 142 (1982): 85-89.

5. E. Jenner, *Inquiry into Cause and Effect of Vaccination* (London: Sampson Low, 1880).

6. J. L. Carrell, *The Speckled Monster: A Historical Tale of Battling Smallpox* (New York: Dutton, 2003).

7. T. Mann, *The Magic Mountain* (New York: Alfred A. Knopf, 1934).

8. M. Thompson, *The Cry and the Covenant* (NY: Garden City Books, 1949).

9. J. Parsonnet and D. Forman, "*Helicobacter pylori* Infection and Gastric Cancer," *JAMA* 291, 2, (Jan 14, 2004): 244-5.

3

The one part of medical practice about which the lay public is most misinformed and about which they hold the most unrealistic expectations is the field of oncology (i.e., cancer practice). Despite the fact that the mortality from heart disease exceeds that of cancer in the United States, the lay public fears cancer much more. It appears to be acceptable to die of heart disease; dying of cancer incites stronger emotions. Perhaps the symptomatology of death from cancer is more frightening. Perhaps because cancer death is progressive, wasting and often painful, lay people fear it more. And yet, deaths due to heart disease can be equally disabling, chronic and symptomatic. Perhaps some education of the public can dispel misinformation and unrealistic expectations about the disease, while at the same time clarify the role of oncology in treating cancer. As we pointed out earlier, if every cancer afflicting people were cured, life expectancy would increase only 2.3 years. Considering the limits of oncology's ability to cure cancer, I wonder why so much of our healthcare expenditures are directed at cancer care. I'll say more about our alleged "progress" later.

As is generally true with most matters of health, the public is bombarded by media messages describing "amazing breakthroughs," "miraculous cures," etc. Unfortunately, much of the current "progress" against cancer is on the level of basic science. It will take many years for the basic science research to be translated into everyday patient care. I have been exposed to media propaganda for forty years of active community hospital pathology practice and have yet to see "amazing breakthroughs." Although chemotherapy is widely viewed as critical to the progress of oncology against many cancers, the resulting yield in survival and quality of life is more hype than measurable progress. People still die of cancer, with or without chemotherapy. As I point out repeatedly, often to the discomfort of my oncology colleagues, "The tumor determines the outcome, not the care."

Although chemotherapy has been extremely effective against some cancers, notably pediatric or embryonal tumors, results against adult cancers have generally been disappointing, or at most, modest. Therefore, oncologists should be highly selective in deciding which tumor to treat with chemotherapy. Chemotherapy should not be indiscriminately administered.

The most common lay error in considering cancer is that cancer is one disease. Nothing can be further from the truth. The notion that we will develop "a cure for cancer" is therefore meaningless. Cancer represents many diseases and we will never find "*a* cure." There are hundreds of different varieties of cancer, and infinite variations within each particular type. Each cancer is a unique disease, with different etiologies (or causes) where they are known, different clinical behaviors, different prognoses (or predictions of the outcome) and different responses to therapy. Some cancers are exceedingly rare; others are relatively common. Therefore, until the basic science of cancer is understood far better, progress against cancer will be incremental, involving many approaches, and occurring over decades of time. The following represents an attempt to describe the many differences among the more common cancers.

FEATURES OF CANCER

Definition of "Cancer"

Cancer cells differ from normal cells in many ways. Whereas normal cells react to stimuli appropriately, cancer cells have inappropriate actions. For example, a normal myocardial (i.e., heart muscle) cell responds to conduction stimuli in the heart, beating at rates appropriate to the body's needs of blood supply. A cancer cell pretty much does what it "wants" to do, and remains unreactive to normal stimuli.

The location of a normal cell is appropriate to its function and that location is fixed. A cancer cell is capable of metastasizing (i.e., spreading) from its site of origin to other body structures, causing damage where it lands. Whereas normal cells have a predictable normal histology (i.e., microscopic appearance) for their location and function, cancer cells differ markedly from normal; the primary location of the cells of certain cases of undifferentiated tumors cannot be identified. The cells of these "undifferentiated" tumors are more prone to metastasize to other sites. The histologic appearance of these metastases often do not indicate the primary source of the tumor.

Normal cells have a defined function and do not interfere with or damage adjacent cells. Cancer cells, on the other hand, damage adjacent cells in a variety of ways, leading to death of normal tissue cells.

Solid versus Multifocal

The most common cancers are solid tumors arising in one organ of the body and, at some point in its lives, metastasize to other sites where a cure is generally unsuccessful. The most fruitful approach to treating a solid cancer is surgical excision of the tumor at its origin in a particular organ, hopefully before it has metastasized. The typical surgical excision involves removal of sufficient normal tissue surrounding the tumor in that organ, so that the tumor excision is considered complete. This is often described as a "cancer operation." The anatomy of the organ involved sometimes determines if excision is an option. For example, surgical removal of a lung cancer may be compromised by the location of the tumor. If the lung cancer is high in the bronchial tree, the surgeon may have to remove an entire lung to complete the excision of the tumor, something the patient may not be able to tolerate. Similarly, if the lung cancer has locally involved important structures in the midline of the thorax (i.e., chest), complete surgical removal is rarely feasible. On the other hand, a colon cancer is ordinarily readily resected (i.e., removed), because the patient can do very well without most of the colon. Similarly, breast cancers are readily resected because breast tissue is not vital to health or body function.

Several cancers are multifocal, arising in many locations of the body. The most common are the various leukemias, or tumors of the white blood cells of the blood, arising in the bone marrow. Typically, much of the bone marrow is involved, so that surgical removal is not a consideration. Tumors of lymphoid tissues, called lymphomas, can be local or multifocal, again limiting surgical removal as the primary form of therapy. These multifocal cancers, because a surgical approach is rarely or never feasible, are treated systemically by chemotherapy, and to a lesser extent, by radiation. Some cancers, despite having already metastasized outside of their primary site in an organ, are treated surgically if it is thought that the metastasis is local enough. This approach again is limited by the affected organ's anatomy. For example, if a colon cancer has metastasized into the local lymph nodes of the mesentery (the fatty support of the colon), the surgeon may remove more than just the colon containing the tumor, hoping that the removal of involved nodes in the mesentery might achieve a better outcome. The pathologic evaluation of these removed nodes might provide critical information about the need for additional therapy. The surgical approach to removing a breast cancer is similar. Although some doubts exist about the therapeutic yield of removing an axillary (i.e., armpit) lymph node metastasis, the confirmation that a lymph node is involved may provide indication for additional non-surgical therapy. Identifying the presence of cancer cells in surrounding lymph nodes is critical to decisions concerning treatment. The presence of lymph node involvement also helps the physician determine the disease's prognosis (i.e., the course of the disease). After all, a cancer which has already spread to regional or local lymph nodes has demonstrated its aggressive potential. When regional lymph nodes are involved, the prognosis of the patient is typically worsened. If many nodes are involved, the prognosis is clearly grim.

Adult versus Pediatric Cancers

The age of the patient is a critical variable in cancer. Some tumors occur only in children. Pediatric (i.e., childhood) cancers usually arise in embryonic structures, tissues normally present in the developing fetus. For reasons that are unclear, these embryonic tissues persist in the infant and have a malignant (i.e., cancer) potential. Example cancers are Wilm's tumors of the kidney, and neuroblastoma of the adrenal, among others. Some of these pediatric tumors are clinically obvious at birth; most present in the first few years of life. A whole group of embryonal tumors—the germ cell (i.e., reproductive) tumors of the testis in young men—occur later in life.

An interesting feature of pediatric tumors is the ability to successfully treat them despite the usually huge size and presence of known metastases. These therapeutic successes have occurred since the introduction of potent chemotherapy drugs. This level of success may be the result of therapeutic synergy, in which the patient's inherent immune response to the cancer combines with the effect of chemotherapy, enhancing the possibility of cure. The infant's body identifies embryonal tissue as "foreign," and mounts an immune response. Truly dramatic therapeutic responses have occurred, both in pediatric cancers and the germ cell tumors of young men. The remarkable case of the competitive cyclist, Lance Armstrong, who has won many international racing events despite having widespread metastatic disease, is a particularly dramatic example. Such synergy does not exist in adult cancers, because the body does not mount an effective immune defense against adult tissue.

These impressive results against pediatric cancers are relatively few; only 2–3 percent of all cancers are of these types. Most cancers arise in adult tissues, and affect patients in increasing numbers as people age. The age of the patient with an adult cancer often determines the clinical course and prognosis. Cancers arising at an age unusual for that tumor are usually more aggressive. For example, colon cancers arising in patients less than forty years of age behave badly. Similarly, breast cancers in young women, particularly premenopausal women, are typically more aggressive than the breast cancers arising in elderly women in their seventies or eighties.

Aggressiveness of Cancer

Great variability exists in cancers arising in different organs and among cancers in a particular organ. Some cancers present clinically as metastatic disease, long before the primary tumor is evident. For example, the long-departed Senator Robert Taft of Ohio had a lung cancer (he was a heavy smoker) which presented clinically as a fractured hip. The bone was the site of a metastasis from the lung, which weakened the bone, and resulted in a spontaneous fracture. A cancer behaving in such a fashion is unusually aggressive, and despite any or all forms of therapy, will kill the patient.

The presence of lymph node spread or spread to other organs is evidence of the aggressive potential of a cancer. The histology (i.e., the microscopic structure identified by a pathologist) of the cancer provides a measure of its aggressiveness. Tumors which are well-differentiated, or histologically similar to the adult normal tissue from which the tumor arose, are typically slow-growing and more amenable to successful therapy. Poorly-differentiated tumors, which microscopically do not resemble the normal organ tissue histologically, are usually far more aggressive. Specific cancers have their own indices of aggressiveness.

Organ of Origin

Perhaps the most important factor in the aggressiveness of a cancer and its prognosis is the organ of origin (Figure 1). At one extreme is cancer of the pancreas, in which the mortality approaches 100 percent. When I was a medical student in the '50s, surgeons abandoned surgical resection because the mortality from the extensive operation was much higher that the possibility of cure. Over the years, as surgical and anesthetic techniques improved, surgeons again attempted resection for a cure. Unfortunately, although operative mortality now is less than 5 percent, surgeons doubt that many cures will be accomplished. Cancer

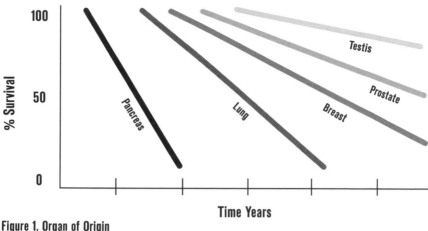

Figure 1. Organ of Origin

of the pancreas may represent *the* worst adult tumor given its overall prognosis. Again, the organ of origin of a particular cancer is one of the prime factors in its clinical behavior.

On the other extreme, certain varieties of thyroid cancer, with or without regional lymph node metastases, have as high a survival rate as that of the population of people without a thyroid cancer. A Mayo Clinic study of the survival of people with thyroid cancer over a forty year follow-up period showed patients with the tumor surviving longer than people without a thyroid cancer.[1] This excellent survival capability with thyroid cancers should tell surgeons to be very conservative with their operative technique in these cases. Further, patients with thyroid nodules can be followed for extended periods without surgery, or at the most, be monitored using a simple needle biopsy. There is little point to engaging in extensive surgery for a cancer with such a good prognosis. Unfortunately, and too often, surgeons will be too eager to remove a thyroid lump, potentially creating problems for their patients. Situated in between pancreatic and thyroid cancers with respect to aggressiveness are the remainder of the solid tumors. Lung cancer has a bad prognosis; no more than 15 percent of all cases survive five years. Surgical resection of lung cancers is often limited by a patient's inadequate lung capacity. Since most lung cancers arise in cigarette smoking patients, the damage to portions of the lung not involved by the cancer precludes large resections for cure. Colon cancers fare better. As many as 50 percent five-year survivals occur, and surgery entails few complications. In colon cancer cases with positive lymph nodes, survival is reduced. In these cases, some slight improvement in survival results from mild combination chemotherapy.

Breast and prostate cancers have even more favorable outcomes. As many as two thirds of breast cancers are cured by surgery. Those patients with involved axillary lymph nodes do not do as well and occasionally benefit from adjuvant chemotherapy. Unfortunately, adjuvant therapy helps only modestly, despite the unrealistic expectations of patients who tend to consider chemotherapy a guarantee of success.

Prostate cancer, very common in men as they age, is a particularly indolent (i.e., slow growing or relatively benign) cancer, consistent with very long survival. As has been said repeatedly, "Men with prostate cancers die *with* prostate cancer rather than *of* it." The benign behavior of most prostate cancers should be an important consideration in screening to detect asymptomatic prostate cancer. This controversial subject will be covered intensively in the next chapter on screening for cancer.

These differences in behavior and survival potential of the several major cancers provide further testimony to the fact that cancer is not one disease; rather, cancers are independent biological entities.

Inheritance of Cancer

An impressive amount of research on the inheritance of cancer has occurred since the mapping of the human genome. Knowledge about the tendency of cancer to run in families has been available for much of the twentieth century. With the ability to map human genes, we can confirm general impressions we've held for years. For example, the inheritance of familial polyposis of the colon had long been defined as autosomal dominant transmission, in which half of a couple's offspring would have the offending dominant gene. Since these patients almost always incur a cancer arising in one of the numerous polyps, removal of the colon at an early age was recommended. Another recommendation, usually not given much credence, was to consider not having children given the disease's 50 percent transmission rate. The unwillingness of people carrying serious genetic abnormalities to forego raising a family is the prime factor in the continuance of these all-too-common inherited diseases.

One of the most useful discoveries in cancer inheritance has been the identification of the BRAC1 and BRAC2 mutant genes in women whose families incur numerous cases of breast cancer. [2] Women with families in which breast cancer occurred in successive generations, or who have breast cancer at an early age, should be tested for these mutant genes. As many as 85 percent of women with these genes will eventually have a breast cancer. The risk of a primary cancer of the ovary is greatly increased in cases of BRAC2 mutation. There is little doubt that more cases of inherited cancers will be identified in the years to come, greatly assisting the control of these inherited conditions.

Geographic and Socio-Economic Factors

We have long known that cancers are more common in the developed and affluent societies of the Western world, clearly implicating potential etiological factors in the environment of the industrialized world. Most of our knowledge of these etiological factors derived from epidemiological studies comparing the Western democracies with the underdeveloped Third World.

Part of the difference in incidence of cancer relates entirely to disparate life expectancies. Third World people die at much younger ages, not achieving the age when cancers tend to become prominent. Beyond that factor are dietary factors which may contribute to the occurrence of certain cancers and explain why cancers of the colon, breast, prostate, and other organs are far more common in the developed world when they are almost unheard of in the Third World. Unfortunately, these epidemiological observations have not been translated into specific etiologic causes. There are too many variables at play when comparing populations to be able to ascertain specific factors.

The most striking population cancer differences have been demonstrated in migrant populations, particularly from Japan to Hawaii and the west coast of the United States.[3] Whereas breast and colon cancers remain relatively uncommon in native Japanese, in just two generations of life in the United States, Nisei developed the same cancer rates as native Caucasians. Similar changes, presumably dietary in origin, have been demonstrated with the passage of time. Breast cancer was rare in Japan prior to World War II. Following the war, as the diet in Japan westernized and included more saturated fats, Japanese girls achieved menarche (i.e., puberty) earlier, were decidedly taller and heavier, and the incidence of breast cancer in Japan increased exponentially. The sole pertinent factor appears to be the change in the diet.

Racial Cancer Differences

Certain cancers are more prevalent in African Americans. Perhaps the best documented is the almost double incidence of prostate cancer in black men as compared to whites. Race, then, may be a factor in determining who ought to be tested for early detection of prostate cancer. The reason for the difference is unknown. For a time, breast cancer was less common in black women than white. This difference has changed, possibly because obesity in some black women contributes to an increase in breast cancer incidence. Socio-economic differences have been described in the etiology of cancer and so may play a role in racial differences of cancer rates. Again, too many variables are involved, confounding the roles of affluence and education. For example, the increased incidence of lung cancer in poor people is clearly related to the high level of cigarette smoking. It is well documented that the higher the education level and affluence, the lower the incidence of cigarette smoking. Smoking has become increasingly a "blue collar" addiction in the lower socio-economic levels of society. Because race, social class, and economic level often overlap, it is difficult to discern the individual role each plays in disease.

Chronological Factors in Cancer

The chronologic graphs (Figures 2 and 3) depict the changing mortality of various cancers over time. These figures depict the number of cancer deaths per year per one hundred thousand people. As is evident, mortality rates of the several common cancers are indicated over the depicted seventy-year interval. The impressive changes in these factors at least hint at the etiologies of the major forms of cancer. Some of the changes have obvious causes. Others are less readily explained.

The striking decline (Figures 2 and 3) in the mortality of gastric (i.e., stomach) cancer is most impressive. Whereas gastric cancer in the first half of the twentieth century killed more American men than any other cancer, it dramatically declined in mortality over a sixty-year period, a

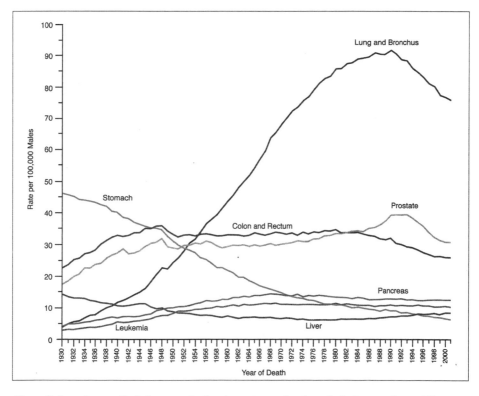

Figure 2. Annual age-adjusted cancer death rates among males for selected cancer types, US, 1930 to 2001.

decrease of more than 80 percent. At one time during my pathology residency at the Minneapolis VA Hospital, we examined two to four new cases of gastric cancer each week. Gradually, over the forty-year period of community hospital practice, my experience with new cases of gastric cancer decreased to less than one case a month. This impressive decline clearly deserves explanation. For many years, because of epidemiologic evidence comparing the developed nations with Third World nations, it was presumed that the improved technology of food preservation—refrigeration and freezing—in the developed world eliminated carcinogen (i.e., cancer-causing agent) production in food preservation. Third World people, lacking refrigeration and freezing for economic reasons, utilized drying, smoking, chemicals, etc., to preserve food. This erroneous conclusion persisted until an Australian pathologist[4] linked the presence of a gastric bacterium, *Helicobacter pylori*, to acid-peptic disease of the stomach and duodenum as well as certain gastric malignancies. Eliminating *Helicobacter* "cured" acid-peptic disease and certain cancers. The incidence of *Helicobacter* colonization has dramatically declined over the years in the developed world, but persists in the Third World because of hygienic differences. We now know that *Helicobacter* decline, not preservation of food, is the reason for the decline in gastric cancer. In a sense, the decline is related to environmental factors, notably the hygienic handling of food.

A similar dramatic decline (Figure 3) in carcinoma of the uterine cervix over the same time period defies explanation. The etiology of carcinoma of the cervix and related inflammatory conditions is well established to be certain strains (or subgroups) of human papillomavirus (HPV), the infection transmitted early in life to females by sexual intercourse.[5] The decline in HPV infection is inexplicable, considering the liberation of sexual mores and practices over the past fifty years. One might expect an increase in HPV infection, rather than a decrease with resulting decline in cancer of the cervix. Whatever the explanation, the decline in this cancer is welcomed. What at one time was the greatest cause of cancer mortality in women is now reduced by 90 percent. I eagerly await a better explanation of this paradox.

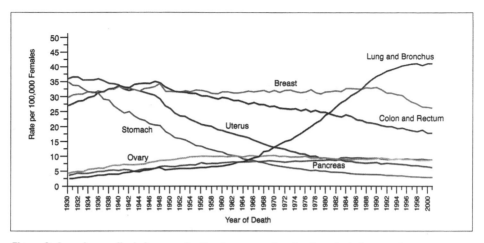

Figure 3. Annual age-adjusted cancer death rates among females for selected cancer types, US, 1930 to 2001.

The female cancer graph (Figure 3) depicts a steady incidence of breast cancer mortality. Over the past fifteen years, beginning at about 1990, breast cancer mortality has modestly declined for a variety of reasons, most of them therapeutic. The incidence of breast cancer has increased; the mortality declined. We will cover this interesting fact further when breast cancer is covered in greater detail.

Colon cancer has also moderately declined (Figures 2, 3) in both men and women over this sixty-year interval. The reasons are unclear, because the decline preceded the utilization of colon cancer screening (a topic covered in the next chapter). The most striking incidence changes in lung cancer for both men and women parallel the increase in cigarette smoking, beginning at least twenty years earlier in men than women. Lung cancer is now the highest cause of cancer mortality in both men and women. Lung cancer mortality passed breast cancer mortality in women about fifteen years ago. Humankind has indeed created a disease.

Prostate cancer mortality in men has moderately increased over the half century, despite a dramatic increase in prostate cancer incidence. The reader should wonder at this paradoxical dramatic increase in incidence and modest increase in mortality. This paradox will be covered in

detail in the next chapter on cancer screening. The other lower incidence cancers have been essentially unchanged over the years and will
not be further reviewed.

Etiology (Cause) of Cancer

One of the most prevalent misconceptions about cancers is that
they are caused by general pollution of the environment by industrial
processes. The latter include energy production pollution from smoke-
stacks; herbicides and pesticides in agriculture; industrial wastes; and
nuclear energy. Although general pollution of the air, soil, and water is
a fact, their role in the causation of the great majority of cancers lacks
substantiation. In truth, the sources of the environmental pollution that
causes the great majority of cancers in the United States are within each
person's control—cigarette smoking, food and alcohol consumption,
sexual incontinence, and sun exposure. The English epidemiologists,
Richard Doll and Richard Peto, from Oxford University, estimate that
these lifestyle factors account for at least 85 percent of cancers.[6] Occupational and other environmental causes count for less than 5 percent
of cancers. This conclusion, of course, is at great variance with the widespread assumption that industrial and other general environmental pollutions are the major causes. Until the public (and medical practitioners
as well) recognize this fact, our efforts at preventing cancer will be compromised. Further, we will expend abundant resources and energy
attempting to control general pollution, whereas the major factor in
cancer causation is under personal control. A simple examination of the
relationship of environmental pollution and the incidence of cancer in
the Western world should provide evidence that general pollution is a
small etiological factor. Whereas general pollution in the environment
tremendously increased throughout the twentieth century, the overall
incidence of cancer remained unchanged. If general pollution was the
prime factor causing cancer, the incidence of cancer should have pro-
portionately increased.

Specific Causes of Cancer

Tobacco smoking unquestionably is the major source of personal environmental pollution that causes cancer. Approximately 450,000 excess deaths occur annually in the United States from diseases related to cigarette smoking. The deaths are not only due to lung and other cancers. Cardiovascular disease, chronic pulmonary emphysema and other diseases are dramatically increased in smokers.

Diet is understood to cause cancer in the developed world. Much of the evidence is epidemiological, comparing the incidence of cancers in the developed and Third Worlds in relation to food intake. Specific relationships have not been identified.

Alcohol consumption is strongly linked to cancer, particularly when combined with cigarette smoking. Many people who abuse alcohol also smoke cigarettes. Cancer of the lung, larynx (i.e., the voice box), esophagus, and pharynx (i.e., the throat) are more common in alcoholics than non-alcoholics. Alcohol causes cirrhosis of the liver, which in turn causes primary cancer of the liver. Obesity directly contributes to breast and endometrial cancers (those of the lining of the uterus).

Radiation exposure very rarely causes cancer. Most diagnostic radiation creates less exposure than ambient cosmic radiation to which all of us are exposed. Some thyroid cancers were caused by radiation exposure in the Chernobyl, Ukraine, atomic energy plant disaster. A few Japanese girls exposed in the atomic blasts at Hiroshima and Nagasaki in 1945 had an increased incidence of breast cancer, but only if they were exposed at menarche (i.e., during puberty).

Some very specific drugs have been incriminated in causing specific rare tumors, when exposure occurred either therapeutically in medical care or on the job. Asbestos exposure has been involved in an increased incidence of lung cancer and mesotheliomas. The latter is a rare tumor, occurring almost exclusively in asbestos-exposed workers.

Sunlight exposure clearly causes damaged skin, leading to an increased incidence of skin cancers and aging phenomena. Sun exposure also contributes to the development of malignant melanoma, a more dangerous skin cancer. The part of the world with the most sun exposure and fair-skinned people, Australia, has the highest incidence of melanoma. Habitués of tanning booths and sun worshipers unwisely are damaging their skin and contributing to an increased incidence of skin cancers. Except for malignant melanoma, most skin cancers are readily treated locally and very rarely metastasize.

BREAST CANCER

One cancer, that of the female breast, deserves a more complete review. Breast cancer is the most common cancer in women, currently second only to lung cancer in its ability to cause cancer death. Although lung cancer kills many more women than breast cancer, breast cancer is often more feared, probably because of the psycho-sexual associations of the female breast. The breast is very much considered a central part of the nature of women. The only biological function of the breasts is nursing infants. And yet, the breast is granted far more significance because of its aesthetic and sexual role in women's lives. This attitude may explain why the current debate on mammographic screening for the early detection of breast cancer has elicited such intense emotions. The value of screening will be covered in the next chapter on screening for cancer.

Incidence of Breast Cancer

There is little doubt that the incidence of breast cancer has increased in recent times in the United States and the Western world. Although breast cancer incidence has increased, breast cancer mortality remains essentially unchanged, at least until about 1990. A modest decline in mortality has occurred since 1990, presumably as a result of improved diagnosis and more effective therapy. There is a decided tendency to credit screening mammography for much of the reduced mortality. This reasoning may commit the logical fallacy *ergo hoc post propter hoc,* in which a causal relationship is proposed between two factors that may in fact be unrelated.

Part of the increase relates to intraductal or in-situ breast cancers, in which the malignancy is confined to the lining of the breast ducts and has not invaded the tissues. This form of cancer is detected by mammography because of the tendency of in-situ cancers to calcify and thus become readily detectable. Although they are histologically defined as cancer, a large number never proceed to invasion and therefore have no potential to become lethal tumors. The in-situ cancers, at least a large number that never proceed to become invasive cancers, are really pathologic curiosities which were better off undetected, and yet detection artificially increases the number of diagnosed "cancers." Once detected by mammography, all in-situ tumors require biopsies, mainly to determine if the in-situ tumor represents a pre-malignant process.

Part of the apparent increase in incidence, particularly in older women, represents more indolent cancers that rarely lead to mortality. The more aggressive breast cancers occurring in younger women have not increased in incidence and represent the majority of breast cancers that cause death. We can conclude this because we can see that the incidence of aggressive tumors, those with involved lymph nodes, has not decreased.

International differences in incidence have been observed in relation to time. The most striking increase has been in Japanese women, an increase clearly related to the dietary and body size changes documented in Japan since the end of World War II.

Etiology of Breast Cancer

It is widely agreed that unopposed estrogen production in women is the primary etiologic factor in most breast cancers. Several factors support this conclusion. Breast cancer never occurs before puberty, apparently because of the lack of an estrogenic stimulus in the pre-pubertal female. Because the initiation of a breast cancer requires the repeated stimuli of the menstrual cycle, breast cancer is extremely rare in the very young. Breast cancer in teenagers is almost unheard of, and less than 1 percent of all breast cancers occur prior to age thirty. Surgical removal of the ovaries in pre-menopausal women reduces the incidence.

The rare cases of women with non-development of the ovaries—ovarian dysgenesis—never have breast cancers.

Increased menstrual life—early menarche or late menopause—causes an increased incidence of breast cancer. The early onset of menarche in Japanese and American girls, probably related to an abundant diet, is related to an increase in incidence.

Obesity, because of its tendency to increase production of estrogen, is believed to play a role in the current increase. The age of the woman having full-term pregnancies affects the incidence as well. Women having full-term pregnancies in their teens or early twenties reduce their risk of breast cancer. Women who delay childbearing until their thirties have an increased risk. The number of pregnancies and the practice of breast feeding reduces the incidence of breast cancer, probably because of hormonal effects. These sociological changes may be contributing factors to the increase in incidence of breast cancer.

The role of genetic inheritance in breast cancer has already been mentioned. It is now believed that hormone replacement therapy for menopausal women increases the risk of breast cancer. Dietary factors, other than those involved in the current epidemic of obesity, have been proposed as significant, but as yet remain undefined.

Prognosis (Prediction of Outcome)

A variety of factors are used to determine the prognosis of a particular breast cancer. Perhaps the most useful is the presence or absence of axillary lymph node metastases. When the lymph nodes are uninvolved, cure rates of 80 or more percent are possible. When nodes are involved, survival likelihood is greatly reduced, depending on other related prognostic factors. Tumors with estrogen receptors (on the cell wall) typically occur in older women and their prognosis is more favorable. The histologic description of a tumor is also useful in prognosis. Tumors which are histologically (relating to their microscopic appearance) well-differentiated tend to be less aggressive and more amenable to effective therapy. These tumors resemble the organ from which they arose histologically. On the other hand, poorly differentiated tumors do not resemble the organ of origin and tend to be more aggressive and less responsive to curative therapy.

Cancer Follow-Up

Although this treatise makes no attempt to discuss cancer therapy beyond its apparent lack of yield commensurate to its cost, one aspect of oncology care is worth mentioning. That aspect is the appropriateness of medical follow-up once primary therapy has been concluded. For reason that have never been convincing to a "doubting Thomas" such as myself, a significant amount of resources and energy are expended on oncology care after surgical resection with or without chemotherapy. This follow-up can be impressively expensive, including a large number of imaging and laboratory tests. Over the years, these additional tests resulted in major increases in costs, particularly when involving the more sophisticated imaging procedures. The number of imaging procedures performed reveals some surprising practices. As one procedure appears to supplant an existing one, one might expect the outdated procedure to be eliminated. Not so! We now often do both because of the rare possibility that the old procedure might detect something not noted on the new test. The evidence to support this is sparse, and yet the number of imaging tests performed increases in an almost exponential fashion. One cannot help but marvel at the ingenuity of radiology equipment manufacturers and radiologists in introducing new and typically more expensive procedures. Some might be uncharitable enough to believe that the reasons for introducing these innovations is merely remunerative. In any event, the newer tests are very expensive. If their use would significantly improve the outcomes of patients with cancer, it would be difficult to question their value. Unfortunately, the improvements appear to be modest at best.

The avowed purpose of cancer follow-up, once primary therapy is complete, is to detect recurrent disease earlier than might occur with a purely clinical approach. We now know that many cancers "recur," despite the claim of surgeons at the completion of the operation that "we got it all." Even the pathological examination of the surgical specimen is unable to guarantee that resection was complete and that recurrence will not occur. This is the nature of cancer. Microscopic foci of tumors, not seen by the surgeon or the pathologist, may seed themselves in the operative site or in distant metastatic locations. The ostensible purpose of follow-up testing is to detect recurrence early, thereby enhancing the chances of benefiting the patient. But does early detection make a difference in the natural course of the disease? Indeed, how much follow-up is required or useful?

From the view of the pathologist, the natural history of recurrent cancer suggests that most traditional oncology follow-up is fruitless and so the suggestion is nihilistic: do nothing. The very nature of pathology practice is the study of the natural history of a disease. This evaluation of causes of cancers provides the pathologist with a superior knowledge base to be able to predict the outcome. When we encounter a tumor which has already metastasized, our training tells us that the future tends to be grim. The best time to cure cancer is with primary surgical resection; even chemotherapy and/or radiation therapy is of slight value only in rare instances. Two possibilities may explain recurrence. First, some tumors are simply too aggressive for the surgical resection to guarantee a cure. No matter how extensive the resection, and no matter how high the level of surgical skill, cure is impossible. Secondly, the handling of tissue during surgical resection may spread the tumor locally or contribute to metastasis. Once a tumor recurs, either locally in the area of the primary site or at a distant metastatic location, "cure" is a rare event. Additional therapy in form of chemotherapy may retard recurrent tumor growth and occasionally improve patient's symptoms, but "cure" rarely occurs. Modern oncology has clear limits to what can be accomplished. Although the lay public and some physicians think that modern chemotherapy can bring about miracles, those instances are extremely rare. Recall the outstanding and apparent "cure" in Lance Armstrong, the Tour de France cyclist who had widespread metastases from a testis cancer. But this tumor is embryonal, and involved a group of cancers in which synergistic therapy is possible. In the vast majority of cases, as we have stated, "The tumor determines the outcome, not the care."

Consider another example of excessive oncology evaluation of a low grade malignant tumor. The patient was an elderly man with extensive past history of serious coronary heart disease, with previous heart attacks and bypass graft surgery. His current problem was a large axillary (i.e., armpit) mass which was a source of discomfort solely because of its huge size. Biopsy revealed a low grade lymphoma, an indolent (i.e., slow-moving) tumor consistent with a long survival, clearly longer than his heart disease would permit. Sophisticated pathology procedures were instituted, none of which could or would alter the original pathology diagnosis. He had a CT body scan to determine the stage of the lymphoma; the result indicated a localized axillary process. The indication for staging was obscure. All the patient required was therapy to reduce the size of the tumor. Effective therapy would have been local radiation or mild chemotherapy. The diagnosis was well established and it was clear that simple therapy would be adequate. Why were the additional studies performed? All that was accomplished was delay of the effective treatment and increased cost. The only justification for the unnecessary additional tests appeared to be that it was "standard" and that "everyone would have done it."

The view I hold is contrary to everyday oncology practices. Oftentimes, much more is done in oncology follow-up than is truly indicated. The rationale seems to be that "everyone does it," or "it is the standard of care," or "if I don't, I will be criticized." The latter expression is typical of defensive medicine. One would think that the amount of excessive and expensive procedures would have been appropriately evaluated, and their cost compared to their yield. In fact, recommendations by the American Society of Clinical Oncology (ASCO) contribute clinical "guidelines" for appropriate follow-up of treated cancer. In particular, ASCO has firm recommendations for follow-up of breast cancer, the most common cancer involving long term follow-up. The ASCO recommendations for breast cancer are almost all office clinical activities: regular history and physical exam, breast exam, and patient education. The only procedure recommended is mammography, because of the known increased incidence of a second tumor in a patient who already had a breast cancer. Specifically not recommended by ASCO are blood counts, imaging of the liver, CT scans, and cancer tumor markers. The fact that so few "procedures" are recommended for most cases may suggest that early detection of recurrence is not beneficial. And indeed it is not.

It would be preferable to wait and see if a recurrence happens. Not only would that avoid the expense, time, and energy involved in performing the "procedures," but those who *are* cured avoid the bother and anxiety of follow-up. Those fortunate patients benefit in two ways; they are cured and they avoid all the proposed follow-up procedures. Some oncologists believe that failing to advocate unindicated procedures in follow-up might be construed as "abandonment." Nonsense! Patients want empathy, encouragement, emotional support, time to talk, not a series of expensive and uncomfortable procedures. Adherence to ASCO recommendations might save billions of increasingly scarce healthcare dollars.

Understanding the role of the "quest for certainty" rounds out our discussion of "appropriate" follow-up of cancer. Robert Petersdorf of the University of Washington discusses this concept, criticizing the desire of some physicians to be absolutely certain that some conclusion or finding in a patient's care is 100 percent correct. One might suggest that this "quest" is a manifestation of physician insecurity, when physicians are unwilling to take even the slightest chance that a conclusion is in error. This sense of insecurity impels him or her to repeat tests or perform additional tests to confirm a preliminary observation. Another possibility is that this behavior reflects medical-legal concerns, and the hope that one or more tests will be ample defense against malpractice litigation. Whatever the reasons, the "quest" expands the use of increasingly expensive procedures at the expense of reasonable and effective medical judgment. After all, there is nothing in the practice of medicine requiring the physician to be absolutely perfect. All that is accomplished by performing an excessive number of tests and procedures is the delay of care, putting the patient at risk for adverse results, and of course, contributing to the expansion of costs.

A typical anecdote may illustrate the problems created by the "quest for certainty." An elderly man presented with a stubborn dermatitis (i.e., chronic skin inflammation) on both legs. Months of using skin oint-ments and taking pills by mouth did not improve the dermatitis. During the treatment for his dermatology problem, his doctors found a hard, large lymph node in his inguinal (i.e., groin) area. Further imaging tests revealed enlarged lymph nodes in the periaortic area (near the spine). A biopsy of the inguinal node confirmed Hodgkin's disease, explaining the stubborn dermatitis. Since this was high stage disease (i.e., several areas were involved), his doctors recommended chemotherapy. Unfor-tunately he did not do well, and suffered several adverse effects of the therapy which his doctors decided to stop. He then received follow-up CT scans (imaging procedures). Although the therapy was inadequate for Hodgkin's disease, it was adequate to "cure" the dermatitis. After several months, another CT scan revealed further enlargement of the lymph nodes. In addition, the severe dermatitis had recurred.

Trying to determine additional therapy, hopefully with less adverse effects this time, the oncologist involved suggested an additional biopsy to confirm recurrent or residual Hodgkin's disease. Several physicians, myself included, questioned the indication for another biopsy. We won-dered what else we could learn. We already had a positive biopsy; the therapy given was clearly inadequate; the dermatitis had recurred; and there was CT evidence of node enlargement. The oncologist argued that the node enlargement could be something else. In other words, despite the fact that we were 99.9 percent certain that the patient had recurrent or residual Hodgkin's disease, and that treatment without another biopsy was perfectly appropriate, the "quest for certainty" required further "proof." The biopsy confirmed Hodgkin's disease; no surprise!

Part of the impetus contributing to the "quest for certainty" is the availability of sophisticated imaging procedures. If CT scans had not been so readily available, it is conceivable that the additional biopsy would not have been performed; clinical judgment might have pre-vailed. Considered generally, not only would this be a superior outcome, but it would save the thousands of dollars that was spent on the unnec-essary additional biopsies. Further, patients would be spared the pain and expense of a second surgical biopsy. Instead of performing unneces-sary tests, the better approach would be to consider the natural history of the disease and to treat accordingly, thereby benefiting the patient and spending healthcare money responsibly.

PROGRESS AGAINST CANCER

If one gives undue attention to media hype, one might get the impression that a "cure for cancer" is just around the corner. As I noted earlier, the idea of *a* cancer cure is, of course, utter nonsense. Each type of cancer is a separate disease, the therapy of which will undoubtedly require different approaches. Before clinical therapy becomes significantly effective, abundant basic science research will be required. Although we are accumulating impressive knowledge about the basic chemistry of cancer, we have a long way to go before effective therapy, beyond surgical removal, will be available. In the meantime, most non-surgical therapy, cytotoxic chemotherapy and radiation therapy, are utilized for advanced cancers. Unfortunately these approaches often damage normal tissues in addition to killing or inhibiting the tumor. The most fruitful current approaches involve using immune mechanisms, which target individual portions of a cancer cell, thus avoiding damage to normal tissues.

Despite the media hype and unrealistic expectations of both physicians and patients, some solid statistical data is available in the literature that places the "progress" against cancer in a more realistic light.

The researcher given the most credit for an honest appraisal of the current "progress" against cancer is John Bailar of Harvard University, a statistician/epidemiologist with impeccable credentials. His 1986 article in the *New England Journal of Medicine* reviewed the incidence and mortality of cancer over the twenty-year period from 1962 to 1982.[7] The incidence and mortality in that period remained the same, suggesting that therapy had little effect on survival. His data confirmed that therapeutic success against pediatric tumors or embryonal cancers in young men were real accomplishments. Unfortunately, these tumors in young people are only a small part of the total cancer picture. Bailar's paper created a major furor, with those in oncology unhappy with the pessimistic conclusion about their efforts. Bailar did not mince words, judging the twenty-year history of cancer "progress" a "qualified failure."

The major argument against Bailar's data was that therapeutic successes still being developed had not yet manifested, suggesting that the passage of time would demonstrate success. Because of the above criticism, Bailar continued his statistical studies at another institution, and published his results in the *New England Journal of Medicine* in 1997.[8] His new title was "Cancer Undefeated." His data covered the years between 1986 and 1994, revealing almost identical cancer mortality over the period. Bailar pointed out that the impressive decline in mortality from gastric and cervical cancer appear unrelated to medical care. At the time of his second publication, the exponential increase in lung cancer mortality in men had not yet plateaued out. His overall conclusion was that "progress" against cancer would involve prevention efforts, not chemotherapy.

John Bailar indeed painted a very pessimistic picture about our obvious lack of "progress" against cancer, at least up until the conclusion of his studies. I hope that he will publish a third edition of his important work in an attempt to identify whether or not improvements in therapy have provided real progress against cancer.

SUMMARY

This chapter attempts to clarify the true yield of oncology care, particularly as it relates to its increasing cost. The first half of the chapter defines cancer for the non-physician reader, attempting to demonstrate that cancer is many diseases with infinite variations.

Dramatic changes in the incidence of the several major cancers have occurred over the past sixty to seventy years, some of which are due to lifestyle factors (such as cigarette smoking) and others due to undefined factors (notably those involved in cancer of the cervix). Knowledge of the role of *Helicobacter* in the etiology (i.e., causation) of gastric cancer is of relatively recent understanding, occurring as a byproduct of research in acid-peptic disease of the stomach and duodenum. The dramatic decline of gastric cancer and its remaining high incidence in the Third World appears due to poor hygienic practices in the latter.

Perhaps the most important information about the causation of cancer derives from the outstanding work of Doll and Peto, which clearly demonstrates that lifestyle factors, completely under control of the individual, are far more important than general environmental factors. Appreciation of this view is critical for society to have in order to address the true etiological factors and to take the emphasis off other environmental pollutions.

The increased incidence of breast cancer is due to both improved diagnostic methodology and changing demography. The improved methodology derives in part from the diagnosis of in-situ cancers, many of which will never become significant cancers but whose identification contributes to the increasing number of incidences. In-situ cancer identification is always due to mammography. The sociologic or demographic changes include late child-bearing and the current epidemic of obesity. The view that the modest decline in breast cancer mortality over the past fifteen years is due to mammographic detection may represent the almost religious support for mammography, ignoring other factors such as improved therapy.

The excessive follow-up of already treated cancer clearly is not indicated and is a major factor in the escalation of oncology costs. It is unfortunate that the outlook for patients with recurrent cancers is so grim. Yet, that reality should not prompt attempts to detect recurrence, when the yield of early detection is miniscule.

The important work of John Bailar should be standard reading for all physicians involved in cancer therapy. Although a pessimistic view of the true accomplishments of oncology, it suggests that the only way to control oncology costs is to appreciate the limits of current oncology care more accurately.

References

1. W. M. McConahey, I. D. Hay, and L. Woolner, "Papillary Thyroid Cancer Treated at the Mayo Clinic, 1946 Through 1970," *Mayo Clinic Proc* 61, 12 (1986 Dec): 978-96.

2. A. R. Venkitaramar, "Cancer Susceptibility and the Function of BRAC1 and BRAC2," *Cell* 108 (2002): 171.

3. J. Cairns, "The Cancer Problems," *Scientific American-Cancer Biology*, (New York: WH Freeman, 1986), 13.

4. A. Covacci and R. Rappuoli, "*Helicobacter Pylori*: After the Genomes," *J Exp Med* 197 (2003): 807.

5. L. Koutsky, "Epidemiology of Human Papillomavirus Infection," *Am J Med* 102, 3 (1997): 3-8.

6. R. Doll and R. Peto, "The Causes of Cancer," *J Natl Cancer Inst* 66, 6 (June 1981): 1191-1308.

7. J. C. Bailar and E. M. Smith, "Progress Against Cancer?," *New Eng J Med* 314, 19 (May 8, 1986): 1226-32.

8. J. C. Bailar and H. L. Gormik, "Cancer Undefeated," *New Eng J Med* 336, 22: (May 29, 1997):1569-94.

4

Screening for Cancer

Many people, including physicians, government officials, members of the media, and members of the public, enthusiastically support the practice of screening for cancer. Much of the fervor behind this support derives from the fear of cancer. People rationalize that any activity designed to lessen the risk of dying with cancer is worthy of support. Hence, early detection of a cancer "makes sense" to many of us. This line of thinking coincides extremely well with Americans' propensity for action. Doing something, whether it has been proved to be of value or not, is often thought preferable to doing nothing.

The concept of early detection is attractive and makes eminently good sense. Solid tumors start small, often microscopically, grow steadily, and at some time metastasize to other parts of the body so that cure is usually impossible or at least unlikely. Theoretically, if the tumor is detected early, surgical removal should be curative if the tumor is confined to its place of origin. This basic tenet in oncology is widely accepted. So there are grounds to the claim that everyone "knows" that early detection is the key to successful cancer therapy. In fact, early detection is the essence of the American Cancer Society's program of cancer control.[1] Since the incidence of cancer is clearly not declining, the next best thing is to detect cancers early enough to cure them. By "early" we mean detecting the cancer before it becomes symptomatic or clinically obvious to both patient and physician. Unfortunately, what "makes sense" must be proven by statistically valid clinical trials. Aye, there's the rub! And unfortunately, most of the currently highly-touted screening tests for early detection of cancer lack the trials necessary to prove that they improve patient outcomes.

A very few of us have had the temerity to question the value of screening for early detection. We have insisted on the performance of random clinical trials (RCTs) to prove that a screening test can do what it is designed to do; namely, reduce mortality for the cancer being screened. Such insistence has generated more heat than light, because of the entrenched medical and popular belief that we "know" that screening is of value and that therefore those who question its value must be mistaken or at least misinformed. This section will therefore examine the evidence for the efficacy of the several screening tests being performed for the most common cancers.

Requirements for Screening

Before a screening test for cancer is implemented into everyday practice, certain basic requirements should be met.

1. The disease for which it tests must be highly prevalent. It would be pointless to screen for rare cancers, because the yield in terms of costs would be very small.

2. The tests must be simple and sensitive. "Simple" implies that the procedure of the tests must be inexpensive and reasonably pleasant. "Sensitive" implies that the test is capable of detecting the cancer being screened.

3. Screening must detect clinically important diseases for which effective treatment is available. It stands to reason that the disease must be amenable to therapy. There is no point to early detection of a cancer in which therapy is ineffective.

4. Finally, early detection should lead to improved outcomes. That is why RCTs are so critical.

A variety of screening tests have been designed to detect the more common cancers affecting humans. Because of the biologic nature of certain cancers, only a few cancers have been studied to see if they can be detected early. The following provides a summary of the evidence available to evaluate the screening potential of the more common cancers.[2]

STOMACH

The rates of incidence and mortality for gastric (i.e., stomach) cancer has been on a steep decline for the past seventy-five years, undoubtedly due in part to the epidemiological decline of *Helicobacter pylori* colonization. As we have pointed out, the unhygienic practices of Third World nations retain a high incidence of *Helicobacter* colonization and therefore continue to have a high incidence of gastric cancer. Because of the prominent decline, no one has recommended screening for early detection. Besides, any screening procedure would necessitate either gastroscopy or contrast medium radiography, both procedures hardly passing the requirement of "simple."

UTERINE CERVIX

Similarly, rates of incidence and mortality for cancer of the cervix have experienced a similar impressive decline for a very long time. The public and many physicians attribute the decline to sensitive Pap smears and subsequent early and effective therapy. However, the decline preceded the widespread utilization of Pap smears by at least thirty years, and therefore, factors other than Pap smears must be responsible. Some argue that the decline would not have continued had Pap smears not become so widely utilized. That argument is fatuous, however, and cannot be proven.

Pap smears are indeed simple, inexpensive and sensitive. However, at least one British study casts serious doubts on the value of the Pap smear in reducing cervical cancer mortality.[3] The British study involved two million women in the Bristol, England, area. The study demonstrated no reduction in mortality from cervical cancer during the period investigated, as compared to historical experience, that is, the period prior to the Bristol study. Of course, using historical experience as a comparison is ordinarily statistically invalid. Nevertheless, this study questions the effectiveness of Pap smears.

An additional problem is the unfortunate byproduct of almost universal Pap smear utilization, namely the frequent finding of cytologic abnormalities due to inflammation, not cancer. These false positive results generate costly additional testing and unmeasurable levels of patient anxiety and also suggest that Pap smears do not yield clean, clear results.

LUNG CANCER

No respectable authority questions the role of cigarette smoking in at least 90 percent of lung cancers and a host of other related malignancies, including those of the pharynx and oral cavity (mouth), larynx, esophagus, and urinary bladder. At best, lung cancer survival is only 15 percent at five years. Instead of early detection, the far better way to control these cancers is to cease cigarette smoking.

A variety of procedures have been developed to establish a screening test capable of detection that is sufficiently early to effect improved outcomes.[4] None has been successful. Frequent chest x-rays and sputum cytology (i.e., microscopic exam of sputum for cancer cells) have been of no value in improving outcomes. The most recent screening technology in smokers, pulmonary spiral CT scan, has been highly touted as having improved imaging resolution, thereby enabling detection of smaller tumors than possible with prior imaging.[5,6] As is unfortunately the case in our healthcare system, this test was highly promoted and introduced with entrepreneurial zeal, long before trials were performed to evaluate its value. Such RCTs have *not* demonstrated improved outcomes. Although the spiral CT scan can detect smaller lesions, mortality is the same as when diagnosis depends on less sophisticated imaging. The reason for this apparent paradox may be related to our lack of understanding of the natural history of lung cancer. It may be that tumor size and mortality outcome are unrelated. That is, metastasis may occur independent of the size of the tumor. A small lung cancer is not necessarily an early cancer.

Despite using techniques that lack clinical yield, free-standing imaging centers have promoted these "improved" CT scans and made them available to well-heeled smokers who walk in and request a study without a physician referral. This creates two problems, besides the critical fact that the procedure does not work. First, the test is indeed more sensitive in its resolution ability to detect shadows in the lungs. Many of these detected findings then demand explanation, creating a host of additional procedures, each contributing to further inflation of healthcare costs. Since not all simple additional tests explain the detected "abnormality," invasive procedures for diagnosis are sometimes mandated.

A rare detected benign process might benefit from early detection. Because of the nature of benign conditions, they can just as well remain undetected, since they'll remain unproblematic. If they will become a problem to the patient, they can readily be treated in the distant future. Howsoever we evaluate screening procedures for lung cancer, the rare benefit to the individual becomes insignificant to the fruitlessness of the great majority of screenings. Again, it is a cost-benefit equation. Clearly the sophisticated CT scan is capable of detecting findings that are better left undetected.

The second obvious problem is providing a false sense of security to the smoker who believes unwisely that the tests will provide early detection of a cancer and ensure a good outcome. The smoker should cease cigarette smoking, not waste his or her money on illusions. Sometime in the distant future, medical technology may develop a better lung cancer screening test, one capable of improving cancer outcomes in smokers. Nevertheless, smoking cessation is the obvious choice of action. For the time being, "medical entrepreneurism" holds sway in the market.

COLON CANCER

Physicians have used a variety of screening procedures over the past few decades in an attempt to detect colon cancer earlier, before its symptoms manifest. Perhaps the earliest attempt was the test to detect blood in the stool, the fecal occult blood test (FOBT).[7] The theory supporting FOBT was that large polyps or cancers of the colon ulcerate and bleed, enabling a chemical test on the stool specimen to detect leaking blood. FOBT suffers from both lack of sensitivity and specificity, however. As noted earlier, a useful screening test should be very sensitive for the disease being screened; very few patients with the disease (colon cancer, in this case) should have a negative test. To avoid an excessive number of false positive test results, FOBT is calibrated to detect 20 ml of blood leaked into the colon each day. Unfortunately, small cancers and premalignant large polyps do not bleed enough to cause a positive FOBT; hence the test has inadequate sensitivity. Cancers large enough to bleed 20 ml per day are usually symptomatic, leading to clinical evaluation, and obviating the purpose of FOBT as an early detection test.

Specificity means avoidance of an excessive number of false positive results. In other words, patients without a cancer should very rarely have a positive FOBT. However, false positives occur. The lack of sensitivity and specificity makes FOBT a very poor early detection test for colon cancer, a position formally stated by the United States Preventive Services Task Force (USPSTF). Despite its lack of value, however, FOBT continues to be promoted by many national organizations and individual physicians. They argue that it "makes sense" or that it is "prudent" to continue using FOBT. What "makes sense" to me is what works, not what is based on vague intuition. Being "prudent" is distinguishing between "doing something" and "doing something worthwhile."

In a similar manner, flexible sigmoidoscopy (visual examination of part of the left colon) has been widely promoted and practiced.[8] The greatest limitation to flexible sigmoidoscopy as a screening tool is its exam limits; most of the colon is not visualized. Again, the USPSTF does not recommend the procedure.

The most recent innovation in screening for colon cancer is the use of colonoscopy, a procedure in which the endoscopist (usually a gastro-enterologist or colorectal surgeon) examines the entire colon under direct vision. Although theoretically an ideal screening test for colon cancer, conventional colonoscopy has several drawbacks. First, the quality of the examination depends on the skill of the endoscopist; false negative studies do occur. Second, unless the colon is completely cleansed of fecal matter in preparation, the examination could be ineffective. Further, the procedure is expensive and requires skilled endoscopists, making logistics of this screening test a problem when it is in high demand. A more recent innovation, obviating the need for a skilled endoscopist, utilizes advanced spiral CT scanning and sophisticated computer software. Unfortunately, the need for scrupulous preparation is the same as with conventional colonoscopy. The new CT scan procedure may be even more uncomfortable, further limiting its value. Perhaps future improvements in this technology will make this innovation a more feasible screening procedure.

BREAST CANCER

The belief that the early detection of breast cancer can improve patient outcomes goes back at least thirty years. Mammography, like the flag, motherhood, and apple pie, is now religiously revered. Observers with the temerity to question its value in the detection of early breast cancers are often viewed with moral indignation and scorn. In my writings on the subject over the years, I have been called insensitive and uncaring. After all, everyone "knows" that mammography is of value in the early detection of breast cancer, and saves many lives. I am far from convinced, however.

Allegedly, mammography can detect a small breast cancer before it can be palpated (i.e., felt) by either the patient or physician. In an average-sized breast, a competent physician can palpate a tumor no smaller than 1 cm in diameter. Technically competent mammography and skillful interpretation may detect a breast cancer possibly half that size though there are notable technical variations in the procedure. Very large breasts, which are difficult to palpate, are better studied with mammograms. Small, dense breasts, particularly in premenopausal women with functioning breast tissue, present mammograms that are difficult to interpret.

These technical variations do not address the fundamental question: Does the use of mammography reduce breast cancer mortality? The question may never be adequately answered, because so much emotion and bias have been introduced into the debate. The mere fact that we are still debating the value of mammography suggests that the issue isn't settled.

One of the earliest studies evaluating the diagnostic usefulness of mammography was performed by the Health Insurance Plan (HIP) of New York, one of the earliest health maintenance organizations (HMOs). In its zeal to demonstrate "health maintenance" in addition to standard medical care, HIP performed a study comparing mammography with standard palpation examinations. [9] The study was large, with sixty thousand women invited to participate, either as the test group (undergoing mammography) or the control (receiving palpation alone). Twenty thousand women elected *not* to participate in the clinical study, apparently for a variety of personal reasons. Twenty thousand women received annual mammograms; twenty thousand had only palpation. At the end of the study, researchers compared the mortality from breast cancer to the total mortality from any cause. The mammography group had a moderately lower breast cancer mortality than did the control group. For reasons unexplained, the control group had a lower total mortality. These results were felt to be an endorsement of the value of mammography in reducing breast cancer mortality; the study was widely quoted. Some time later, an inquisitive investigator asked what happened to the twenty thousand women who elected *not* to participate in the study. Fortunately, HIP follow-up and record keeping was excellent, enabling valid evaluation of this non-participant group. The surprise finding was that the non-participants had a lower breast cancer mortality than either the mammography group or the controls. [10] For unknown reasons, this group of non-participants had better experience than either the tested mammography group or the group receiving palpation alone.

Götzshe and Olsen Study

Since the HIP study some thirty years ago, several large, additional studies from around the world have been reported, including work from Canada, Sweden and the United States.[11] Generally, the results of these studies supported the use of mammography, some suggesting that breast cancer mortality could be reduced by as much as 30 percent with mammography. Those with some appreciation of the doubling times of tumor growth and the potential limits of mammography viewed this figure as unbelievable. Nevertheless, mammography became a standard form of screening for breast cancer and was endorsed by almost all relevant oncology and radiology organizations. Only pathologists truly realistic about the behaviors and courses of cancers continued to raise doubts.

Peter Götzshe and Ole Olsen, Danish researchers affiliated with the Cochrane Collaboration, a highly respected British think tank, ventured into the morass of the debate with an article in *Lancet*, the respected English medical journal.[12] Their investigation stimulated an international furor in mammography circles, because they concluded that most studies didn't support the use of mammography. In fact, this conclusion was so dramatic that the Cochrane Collaboration tried to avoid responsibility for the studies. The Götzshe and Olsen work was stimulated by a prior Swedish study, one suggesting that the use of mammography had not materialized the expected decrease in breast cancer mortality. They examined the statistics of seven major studies, five of which had extolled the value of mammography. Two studies had concluded that its value was very doubtful. The five positive studies had major statistical biases that were sufficient enough to negate the value of the conclusions. The most frequent bias was inadequate randomization of the study groups, so that mammography patients were inadequately matched against controls. Two studies, one carried out in Mälmo, Sweden, and the other a huge Canadian trial, concluded that mammography was of no value in reducing breast cancer mortality.[13,14] These latter studies, although far from statistically perfect, were deemed to be of "medium" quality and therefore more in tune with the truth. A heated series of rebuttal publications ensued, but the two Danish investigators have not reversed their position.

False Positive Mammograms

In addition to the negative conclusions of the Götzshe-Olsen study, the adverse effects of false positive mammograms has raised concern. A review of annual mammography over a ten-year period showed that as many as one-fourth of women receiving mammograms would have had at least one false positive.[15] False positives mandate additional studies, including biopsies, all of which induce intense patient anxiety. Although the women who learn that their false positive was found to be benign and are therefore delighted and relieved, the anxiety, discomfort, and expense of the additional evaluations cannot be downplayed.

The problem of false positives from screening tests is certainly not limited to mammography. Any screening test may yield such results. The possible value of mammography, if demonstrated, must be balanced against the negative aspects of false positive studies. The primary concern of medical practice, *Primum non nocere (First, do no harm)*, should be part of any consideration of the value of screening tests. That is, the relief achieved by the woman who learns that her abnormal mammogram was due to some benign or otherwise unimportant finding must be balanced by the expense and anxiety of a false positive study.

And as we know, there is scant evidence to support the view that the early detection by mammography necessarily saves lives. Studies by Götzshe and Olsen and others strongly suggest this. If these negative studies do not confirm a reduction in breast cancer mortality as evidenced by population studies, then any advantage to the individual is not substantiated.

Current State of Mammography

Neither Götzshe and Olsen nor other doubting Thomases have influenced the practice of mammography significantly. Far too much emotion is involved in the debate. Cancer organizations, support groups, radiologists, and others accept its value as established and regard questions about its value as absurd. The practice of mammography is so well-entrenched that ordering them has become the law of the medical land. If it indeed offers a breast cancer survival advantage, the improvement is modest at the very best.

The recent improvement in breast cancer mortality these past fifteen years has been attributed to early detection by mammography. It is unclear to me why this particular variable in the process earns so much credence. This could easily represent the logical fallacy, *post hoc ergo propter hoc,* in which unrelated observations are mistakenly assumed to have a cause-and-effect relationship. Therapy of breast cancer has improved with novel immune and chemotherapy approaches. Why would not therapy be as much responsible for the mortality improvement as mammography?

PROSTATE CANCER

Introduction

For reasons that may be more apparent to lay people than to physicians, the discussion of the value of screening for prostate cancer is not as emotional as those addressing the value of mammography. Perhaps it is because prostate cancer occurs in an older population of men where the public attitude is, "You have to die of something." In contrast, breast cancer mortality tends to occur in a woman's middle years and involves an organ with strong psycho-sexual meanings. The breast is physically obvious and is a distinguishing feature of women. Another reason may simply be that the prostate is a hidden organ, the purpose and function of which is unknown to most men and women. The prostate has little more biological function than the breast. All it does is provide the liquid medium for ejaculation of sperm for reproductive purposes. In older men beyond the age of reproduction, it has essentially no purpose. The sole exception is to serve as a means of livelihood for urologists treating its disorders.

The therapeutic considerations of treating prostate cancer, though, are far more significant than those for treating breast cancer. Surgical approaches to treating prostate cancer are far more formidable than breast biopsies or even mastectomy. The female breast is largely an appendage of the skin, with relatively minimal function. Surgery on the breast is readily performed with minimal morbidity and very rare mortality. On the other hand, prostate cancer therapy, mainly because of the location of the gland, involves impressive surgery with significant operative morbidity and major postoperative complications (at least for some). Urinary incontinence, even when short-lived, is a serious consequence to prostate cancer surgery. Sexual impotency, particularly in the younger, sexually active man, can be a devastating complication. Breast surgery doesn't involve comparable problems.

Among physicians involved in treating prostate cancer, controversy about the benefits of screening has stimulated a vigorous debate, some of which can involve laymen who become involved personally. The intensity of the prostate cancer screening debate, similar to those about many other medical interventions, has been complicated by the typical American propensity for action. Instead of studying the screening activities' value objectively, we have permitted emotion and the propensity to "do something" to take over and be translated into activity. This behavior is typical of those inclined to "Don't just stand there. Do something." thinking. The lay public does not accept the advice that a particular cancer might do as well with "watchful waiting" as with radical surgery. If a patient is told he has a prostate cancer, no matter what his age, he wants it treated. Unfortunately, because of the serious consequences of the diagnosis of prostate cancer, therapy might do far more harm than good: the potential modes of therapy for prostate cancer frequently do more damage to the patient than the possibility of a cancer cure. As a result of our advances in screening detection, thousands of men have undergone major surgery for a condition which would never have been a clinical problem or a cause of premature death.

I have personally become involved in the prostate cancer screening debate, at least on the local level. I have engaged "experts" on the question in lectures to medical audiences and in publications. When one of my medical articles on screening was reprinted (with permission, of course) in another journal, I did not realize that some of the readers of the other publication were lay people. One man who had a radical prostatectomy read my piece and complained vociferously to his urologist, claiming that he had been subjected to unnecessary surgery. He no longer had sexual potency. That observation led to heated correspondence between the editor of the reprinting publication and me. I was verbally attacked as "a traitor to the profession" and "a loose cannon on deck." Fortunately, I am endowed with the skin of an alligator and the heated exchanges eventually ceased. I had been attacked instead of the real problem: the logical fallacy, *ad hominem*, is not an appropriate move in serious discussion.

PSA Testing

Prostate-specific antigen (PSA) is a unique and specific substance secreted only by prostatic epithelium. Huge levels of PSA are present in semen, a reflection of the sole purpose of the antigen. The identification of PSA, particularly because of its unique origin solely in the prostate gland, led to its original use in following the course of therapy for an already-diagnosed prostate cancer. Physicians had established that digital rectal examination (DRE) was of very limited value in making a diagnosis of prostate cancer. PSA testing was also used to confirm diagnosis of cancer based on palpation of the gland, since benign inflammatory conditions, particularly chronic inflammation, can feel as abnormal to the palpating finger as a cancer. Another positive feature of PSA testing as a screening test is its ease of performance and modest expense. PSA testing involves a simple and very reproducible blood test, which most clinical laboratories can perform readily for a modest fee. Finally, it was learned that prostatic epithelium affected by a prostate cancer produces more PSA than normal prostate epithelium, thereby providing a useful diagnostic parameter.

Although the above suggests that PSA testing is an ideal screening test for prostate cancer, nothing could be further from the truth. Although prostate cancers typically have elevated serum PSA values, the test lacks both sensitivity and specificity, statistical criteria of validity necessary required of any good screening test.

Although the lack of sensitivity and specificity have long been recognized in PSA screening, most of the research had been done on men with elevated PSAs. A recent study, published in the *New England Journal of Medicine*, reported on the prostate needle biopsies of men who had repeatedly normal PSA levels over a period of seven years.[16] Ordinarily, these men with normal PSA values would not have been biopsied. To the surprise of many, 15 percent of the needle biopsies were positive for prostate cancer, many with PSA levels in the low normal range. Biopsies in the high normal range were positive in 25 percent of cases. By any definition of sensitivity, these numbers show the test to be inadequate. If many men have a prostate cancer and yet have normal PSA, of what value is the screening test?

Similar questions of specificity arise. Men with enlarged but benign glands and men with prostatitis often have elevated PSA levels. In an effort to improve the sensitivity of the PSA test as a screening tool, some experts suggest lowering the range in which levels are considered normal. This would only increase the number of biopsies performed, since the PSA test would probably detect low-grade cancers, which represent insignificant disease. Despite having only low-grade or "insignificant" cancers, many men thus have radical treatment, and suffer all its undesirable side effects.

Diagnostic Tests

Despite its inadequacies, PSA tests often currently lead to diagnostic ultrasound (US) and needle biopsies. The relative ease and precision of the combined US and biopsy gun procedures have undoubtedly contributed to the number of positive biopsies and resulting major therapies. Hence, the combination of simple screening and the availability of relatively easy biopsy procedures have combined to increase the number of prostate cancers diagnosed dramatically. Some groups, particularly those whose professional activities are increased by treating prostate cancer, believe this outcome to be the "best of all possible worlds." However, the benefit to practitioners with increased caseloads cannot outweigh the cost to the elderly men whose lives are altered by therapy and who incur little benefit.

Epidemiology of Prostate Cancer

Over the past fifteen to twenty years, as a direct result of the use of PSA screening and the high rate of biopsies, the incidence of prostate cancer has increased dramatically. One study reported 230,000 men with a new diagnosis of prostate cancer each year in this country, while only thirty thousand are expected to die from the disease. Further, despite the dramatic increase in prostate cancer diagnoses, mortality has been unchanged. Some believe that as many as seven out of eight cancers are insignificant; those men will die *with* a cancer, not *of* the cancer. This is not to imply that prostate cancer is insignificant; it is the second highest cause of cancer mortality in men. However, there is little or no evidence that early detection by screening will save lives. In the meantime, and despite these figures, an unfortunately high number of men will be treated for a disease without apparent benefit and with major undesirable side effects.

Prostate cancer screening is predominantly an American phenomenon. PSA screening is rarely performed in Great Britain and an increase in prostate cancer diagnosis has not been documented in England and Wales. Despite the lack of screening, the mortality from prostate cancer in the United Kingdom is unchanged. Similar data is available from the other European nations.

Another fascinating phenomenon is the gross differences in prostate cancer screening and therapy within the United States. PSA screening and subsequent radical therapy for prostate cancer is a much more common practice in the Pacific Northwest and Alaska. If a man resides in New England, he is much more likely to retain his prostate than if he lived in these other areas. At the same time, his chances from dying from prostate cancer are no higher. There is no shortage of urologists or radiation therapists in New England to explain this disparity. One might be labeled old-fashioned if one believes that the disease should determine the management, not practice styles in a particular area. So call me old-fashioned.

The above epidemiologic disparities have been emphasized by major organizations involved with cancer. The U.S. Preventive Services Task Force (USPSTF) said in a position statement, "evidence is insufficient to recommend.... screening;" this is clearly a negative recommendation.[17] Similar reluctance to support PSA screening has come from the Canadian counterpart of USPSTF. As I pointed out previously, most of Western Europe and the rest of the world view PSA screening as an American phenomenon that lacks evidence of any value. One English oncologist described PSA testing in the "colonies" as a "prostatic Holocaust."

The sole USPSTF recommendation supporting PSA screening addresses the situation of black men or men with a family history of prostate cancer. The USPSTF would also limit screening to men between fifty and seventy years of age, and would not screen anyone with anticipated life expectancy of less than ten years.

Three major studies of the natural history of prostate cancer are in progress. Whether these studies will answer the many unanswered questions is debatable, considering the heterogeneity of the disease.

Natural History

As is unfortunately so often the case, the natural history of prostate cancer, when left untreated, is not known. Until medical practice understands a disease's actual history, we cannot determine effective therapy. This problem is present in spades for prostate cancer. Autopsy studies of men who died of other conditions have demonstrated a gradual increase in the incidence of prostate cancer throughout life. Although we ordinarily think of prostate cancer as an old man's disease, cancers have been seen in young men, as early as those in their twenties. This finding indicates clearly how slow-growing this cancer is, because clinical prostate cancer is not a young man's problem. As many as half of men in their eighties have a prostate cancer. In fact, some say that every male will have a prostate cancer if he lives long enough. This evidence of the generally indolent nature of most prostate cancers should give pause to physicians involved in the diagnosis and therapy of prostate cancer. A Swedish study of older men with established diagnoses of prostate cancer revealed that "watchful waiting" (i.e., doing nothing) was as effective as radical prostatectomy.[18] Further, the study demonstrated that the progression of a cancer very often could be controlled by a pharmaceutical approach, mainly involving drugs suppressing androgens. As I've said, "Old men die *with* prostate cancer, rather than *of* it."

The histologic grading of the tumor, as described by Dr. Donald Gleason of the Minneapolis VA Hospital, fills in part of the natural history of prostate cancer. Low-grade prostate cancers, Gleason has found, are consistent with very long survival and little clinical disease effect from the tumor. High-grade tumors, because they are also usually large, have a bad outcome no matter what is done.

Summary of Prostate Cancer

Of all the screening tests proposed for screening cancer, that for prostate cancer may be the most problematic. It is painfully clear that the current PSA screen is equivalent to the tail wagging the dog. The available screening technology, without a clear picture of the natural history of prostate cancer, creates a situation of excessive diagnosis and potentially harmful and excessive therapy. Prostate cancer is a very variable and common disease. The great majority of diagnosed incidences of this cancer will never be a significant problem for or cause of death in men. Unfortunately, practice styles in the United States and the reaction of lay people to any cancer diagnosis lead to inordinate levels of formidable therapy, with a great potential to doing harm. What is needed, along with better knowledge of the natural history of the disease, are new biomarkers enabling the physician to separate the cases requiring serious therapy from the more numerous cases of little or no significance to the patient. Such markers appear to be slow in coming. Until they are available, we should be very cautious about recommending radical therapy for a disease the full course of which is unknown and the seriousness of which is so debatable.

SUMMARY

The value of screening for early detection of cancer is a matter of debate among members of the medical community. The public view about its value is unequivocal: it "makes sense." Part of the lay enthusiasm for the value of screening derives from the desire of lay people to "do something," a typically American trait. Acceptance by several prestigious medical organizations, and by physicians in general, and oncologists in particular, contributes to the belief in the value of screening. Unfortunately, what "makes sense" must withstand the scrutiny of controlled clinical trials. That is where the debate begins. In so many instances, screening techniques are put into practice before the procedure has been evaluated scientifically. Often, early attempts to support its value scientifically lack statistical validity. Finally, everyday medical practice continues using these tests, whether or not they've been evaluated adequately, either because nothing better is available or because they believe that the screening procedure has assumed the aura of "standard of care."

Only a handful of the more common adult cancers have reliable and good screening tests. Despite the fact that lung cancer is responsible for the most cancer deaths in both men and women, it has no single screening test. The disease appears to be so inherently aggressive that the several attempts to screen for lung cancer have thus far been unsuccessful. Attempting to limit screening tests to some group at greatest risk—cigarette smokers—also has not been successful. Unfortunately, despite the fact that studies have not supported its value, spiral CT scans have been promoted aggressively by entrepreneurial groups catering to well-heeled smokers.

Screening for cervical cancer using Pap smears is generally accepted as a simple and useful procedure. However, Pap smears unfortunately detect benign inflammatory conditions that demand further study. Nevertheless, the Pap smear has achieved general acceptance as an adequate screening test for cervical cancer.

Stomach cancer, because its incidence has dramatically declined over the past half century, is not a candidate for screening. Only breast, colon, and prostate cancers are now candidates for screening. Despite widespread practice for all three, much debate remains about their efficacy in detecting the cancers early enough to reduce mortality.

Colorectal cancer has been screened for by fecal occult blood testing and sigmoidoscopy for decades and has never achieved legitimate results. The only test accepted by most authorities is colonoscopy. Problems intrinsic to this test, namely expense and discomfort, reduce its value. Perhaps the newly introduced "virtual" colonoscopy, an imaging procedure, may turn out to be an improvement.

Breast cancer screening by mammography, although widely accepted with an almost religious fervor, remains controversial. The procedure undoubtedly suffers from yielding an excessive number of false positive tests, contributing to expense and anxiety. Further, several of the studies supporting its value in reducing breast cancer mortality have been criticized on statistical grounds. After fifty years of mammography, we are still debating its value. We may never learn the value of mammographic screening, mainly because its proponents are too well entrenched in their positions.

Prostate cancer potentially is the most problematic screening test. The intensity of the debate of its value is impressive. Despite ongoing discussion on the American medical scene, the screening procedure is used almost universally. The unfortunate aspect of PSA screening for prostate cancer is the number of positive detections it yields. The great majority of detected prostate cancers will never be a significant problem to patients. However, once detected, the steamroller of therapeutic activity often becomes unstoppable. Most prostate cancer therapies have serious adverse effects. Since the natural history of prostate cancer is only partially appreciated, current therapeutic activity may engender a great deal of harm for a disease that may have a benign and insignificant course.

References

1. S. Handler, "The Futility and Lack of Cost-Effectiveness in Screening for Cancer," *Minn Med* 75, (December 1992): 17-19.

2. R. S. Fontana, D. R. Sanderson, and L. Woolner, "Cancer Statistics 1991," *CA* 41 (1991): 19-36.

3. A. E. Raffle, B. Alden, and R. Mackenzie, "Detection Rates for Abnormal Cervical Smears: What are We Screening For?," *Lancet* 345 (June 10, 1995): 1469.

4. T. L. Petty, "Screening Strategies for Early Detection of Lung Cancer," *JAMA* 284, No. 15 (October 18, 2000): 1977-80.

5. S. J. Swensen, et al., "Screening for Lung Cancer with Low-Dose Spiral CT," *Am J Resp and Crit Med* 165 (2002): 508-513.

6. P. J. Mahadevia, L. A. Fleisher, et al., "Lung Cancer Screening with Helical CT in Older Adult Smokers," *JAMA* 289, No. 3 (January 15, 2003): 313-22.

7. T. F. Ransohoff and C. A. Lang, "Screening for Colorectal Cancer," *N Eng J Med* 325 (1991): 37-41.

8. J. V. Selby and G. D. Friedman, "Sigmoidoscopy in the Periodic Health Examination," *JAMA* 269 (1989): 595-601.

9. S. Shapiro, W. Venet, et al., "Ten to Fourteen-year Effect of Screening on Breast Cancer Mortality," *J. Nat Cancer Inst* 69 (1982): 349-55.

10. P. Skrabanek, "False Premises and False Promise of Breast Cancer Screening," *Lancet* 2, No. 8450 (1985): 316-20.

11. L. Taber, C. J. Faberberg, et al., "Reduction in Mortality From Breast Cancer After Mass Screening," *Lancet* 1, No. 8433 (1985): 829-32.

12. P. Götzshe and O. Olsen, "Is Screening for Breast Cancer with Mammography Justifiable?," *Lancet* 355 (2000): 129-34.

13. I. Andersson, K. Aspergren, et al., "Mammographic Screening and Mortality from Breast Cancer, the Malmo Trial," *Brit Med J* 297 (1988): 943-48.

14. C. J. Baines, "The Canadian National Breast Cancer Study," *Ann Int Med* 120 (1994): 326-34.

15. J. G. Elmore, et al., "Ten-Year Risk of False Positive Screening Mammograms," *N Eng J Med* 338, No. 16 (April 16, 1998): 1089-96.

16. I. M. Thompson, et al., "Prevalence of Prostate Cancer Among Men with a PSA Level Less Than 40 mg/ml," *N Eng J Med* 350, No. 22 (May 27, 2004): 2238-2246.

17. R. Harris and K. N. Lohr, "Screening for Prostate Cancer: An Update of the Incidence for the U.S. Preventive Services Task Force," *Ann Int Med* 137, no. 11 (December 3, 2002): 917-31.

18. J. Johansson, H. Adami, et al., "High Ten-Year Survival with Untreated Prostate Cancer," *JAMA* 267 No. 16 (April 22/29, 1992): 2191-6.

5

Role of Environmental Pollution in Human Disease

Discussion of the role of environmental pollution in the etiology (or cause) of human disease stimulates an almost universal response. The lay public is firmly convinced that pollution of the environment by industrial processes is responsible for a host of diseases, particularly cancer and birth defects. When I addressed the subject a short while ago at a meeting of the American Association of University Women (AAUW), I began by asking for a show of hands from those who believed that the assumption is correct. Over 95 percent of the AAUW group raised their hands. Given this kind of widespread belief, any person with the temerity to suggest otherwise is vilified as some kind of "right-wing nut." After all, everyone "knows" that environmental pollution causes much of our human disease disorders, and if we clean up the environment, it is obvious that cancer and birth defects will be reduced.

This is a popular and almost universal position. However, the connections between environmental pollution and disease are not supported by evidence. As we discussed earlier in the section on cancer, Bailar and others demonstrated that both the incidence and mortality of cancer have remained unchanged for decades.[1] Since environmental pollution increased dramatically through much of the twentieth century, we should have seen an overwhelming increase in the incidence of cancer if a connection existed. A similar line of thinking exists about birth defects, which also are attributed to environmental pollution. Yet the incidence of birth defects has remained constant at 5 percent of births throughout the twentieth century, despite the increase of pollution. Not only is the connection between pollution and disease inaccurate, but the conclusion that they are connected serves only to create public anxiety. People live in constant fear of cancer or seeing birth defects in their children. Because of this misleading conclusion, we remain ignorant of the real factors causing human disease. As a result, we expend fruitless and expensive efforts, most of which result in no benefit to society. This section will examine some of the worst examples of wasteful efforts.

Certain elements of our society are particularly responsible for contributing to this misinformation. Some groups are reasonably informed, but nevertheless continue to propagate the "myth" despite knowing better. Other groups prosper in economic ways from connecting environmental pollution with disease. Still others make the connection for ulterior motives, hoping to enhance an economic or political agenda. I will discuss three groups in particular: the media, government, and a small but influential fringe of the environmental movement. I include the latter with serious trepidation, mainly because environmentalism is akin to motherhood, the flag, and apple pie. I would emphasize that the major accomplishments of environmentalists in cleaning up our air, water, lakes, are impressive. A small segment of the movement, specifically activists called "apocalyptics," have an anti-business and anti-development agenda. This group has found associating pollution with disease useful in furthering their cause and have little reluctance in distorting the truth. These groups include the Natural Resources Defense Council and the Center for Science in the Public Interest, among several others.

THE MEDIA

The media are notorious in presenting misinformation about health issues. Anything dramatic, new, or frightening is newsworthy, and regarded as capable of selling newspapers or television time. Although factual information about health issues is available in the serious print media, medical literature, and public television, these entities do not enjoy sufficient public exposure to be influential. Examples of medical misinformation are regularly aired on the six o'clock television news, which regularly describes "medical breakthroughs," "miraculous cures," "amazing new studies," and "cutting edge technology." Despite the fact that these "breakthroughs" often involve only a handful of cases, or represent preliminary data, or have not been subject to review or repetition, they are portrayed as major advances in healthcare. The media also present anecdotes as representative of established fact. Some of the "breakthroughs" may involve basic science advances which will not be of clinical value for fifteen to twenty years, and yet are portrayed as something available next week. News that these "advances" are subsequently disproved or no longer credible, is either ignored or buried in back pages. Certain lay publications, particularly periodicals catering to women, are infamous for their hypocrisy. The same journal issue supporting the value of alternative care or "exposing" some theoretical environmental concern, will have several full-page advertising spreads relating brands of cigarettes to youth, fun, glamour, and the good life.

Yellow Journalism

Although examples are legion, two examples of "yellow journalism" may make the point. The CBS television program 60 Minutes is notorious for presenting biased and highly edited misinformation as fact. This sensational reporting may account for its popularity. Some time ago, Meryl Streep, an actress-turned-alleged-toxicologist, presented information about Alar in a 60 Minutes episode. Her report on Alar characterized Alar as "an intolerable risk" for cancer in children. Alar had long been used to retard ripening of apples, thereby reducing spoilage and making apples less expensive. Newer assay technology was able to demonstrate trace amounts of Alar on marketed apples. No clinical information about human damage was available, and yet, without any evidence, the CBS program damaged the apple industry for years. Subsequent studies demonstrated that Alar presented no health hazard to children or anyone else.[2] Elizabeth Whelan in her book Toxic Terror described the cost to the apple industry of this misinformation. CBS knew that Ms. Streep had no credentials as a toxicologist and that she had connections with environmental movements. And yet they presented this harmful program as factual and did a great deal of harm. The children who should have been eating apples as good food were deprived of them due to this misinformation.

Another blatant report of misinformation was presented by the CBS program *Face the Nation*. Connie Chung presented an exposé on silicone breast implants, using a series of anecdotes by tearful and distraught women.[3] Other than using undocumented testimonials that lacked scientific proof, Ms. Chung and CBS presented a connection between silicone breast implants and disease as established fact. Several well-performed studies have demonstrated *no* etiological (i.e., causative) relationship between the implants and a host of unrelated immune and connective tissue disorders.[4] These studies clearly indicate that the incidence of these disorders is no higher in the patients with implants than in the general population. Despite the solid epidemiological data, class action litigations extorted billions of dollars of blackmail settlements from the implant manufacturers. The truth has never deterred avaricious plaintiff lawyers from extracting their toll from innocent manufacturers.

Fortunately, after a thirteen-year FDA ban on silicone breast implants, the forces of science will prevail over the forces of anti-science. It is now obvious that silicone implants are solely a local breast problem, without any risk of systemic disease. It would be nice if Connie Chung and CBS would retract their story. It would be a miracle if the plaintiff attorneys would return the settlement money they extorted from the implant manufacturers by unsubstantiated claims.

GOVERNMENT MISINFORMATION

Government on all levels is capable of providing misinformation about environmental health issues, thus creating public panic and anxiety and generating useless legislation and bureaucracy. Elected officials respond readily to sensational misinformation provided by hopefully well-intentioned environmentalists who allege that some environmental pollution is a health hazard. Without solid epidemiological or other scientific data supporting the risk, legislation is passed that inhibits significantly the use of agricultural and other industrial products. The proposed legislation readily passes because it costs government very little and enhances the legislator's reputation with the voters as protecting the public from harm. Some of the "protective" legislation is worded vaguely, enabling regulatory bodies to interpret the law in very strict terms. What originally was designed to "protect" the public from danger becomes a major cost factor for business and industry without benefiting the public. Because of hasty and irrational rules and regulations, farmers and industries are prevented from using perfectly safe chemical products and are forced to use expensive and less effective alternatives. The public pays for the added expense without incurring benefit. Examples of such ineffective government activity follow.

The Delaney Clause

Congressman Delaney introduced an amendment to other legislation relating to food additives in 1958. Delaney was apparently convinced by some imaginative environmental "apocalyptics" that food additives could cause human cancers. The amendment (The Delaney Clause) mandated that any food additive, in any dose, which caused cancer in any laboratory animal, would be banned. The Clause epitomized the philosophy that a rat is a small person and that what happens to rats must happen to people. This concept subsequently spread to agricultural pesticides and herbicides and to trace levels of chemicals in general use. The amendment created by Delaney resulted in rules and regulations issued by the EPA and FDA. Billions of dollars are expended in compliance, and all for naught. Not only has improved analytic technology been able to detect trace amounts of chemicals, but nobody has demonstrated with appropriate human epidemiologic studies that any harm or disease has been related to these chemicals.

Fortunately, reason and science now prevail, and the worst aspects of the Delaney Clause are being withdrawn or modified. We must think rationally, rather than react with fear of some "possible" environmental hazard. Society is not benefited by the desire for a completely risk-free environment, especially with regard to cancer.

Superfund

Superfund was created to reduce the risk of cancer in people exposed to toxic waste sites.[5] Up until a few decades ago, disposal of toxic wastes in industrial sites was haphazard and clearly inadequate. Companies generating toxic wastes regularly discarded toxic chemicals on the company's grounds with little concern for the future. It was economically "convenient" to dump wastes in the ground, taking little or no effort as would appropriate disposal. Unfortunately, businesses failed or relocated, resulting in toxic waste accumulations which were never a problem for the original business. When these unwise practices were exposed, Superfund legislation, designed to clear up thousands of designated toxic waste sites, was enacted. The legislation was well intentioned; its execution was much less impressive. Experience with the process of transferring soil from toxic waste sites to appropriate disposal facilities turned out to be a very formidable and expensive task. Although billions of dollars are spent annually in the project, very few sites have been cleaned completely. The contamination of the soil was far more extensive than anticipated.

Fortunately, some level-headed epidemiologists have asked some incisive questions about Superfund. First, is the documented exposure of people to toxic waste a significant health hazard? If not, are there less expensive and equally efficacious ways to handle the problem? The first question was answered readily. Health surveys of persons living in proximity to toxic waste sites demonstrated that those individuals suffered no increase in incidence of cancer or birth defects. Apparently, people are tougher than presumed and can tolerate significant exposure to toxic materials. If this is true, then the environmental clean-up problem becomes an aesthetic rather than a disease-causing problem. Instead of completing the overwhelming process of transferring contaminated soil to appropriate disposal facilities, it would be far simpler and clearly less expensive to cover the sites with soil and grass. Further, if the exposure is indeed not harmful to exposed persons, the aesthetically improved sites could be converted to less polluting business functions.

The sad result of the Superfund efforts was to create public panic and anxiety. People living in identified toxic areas are convinced that they will die of cancer or have three-headed children. After all, if the government is working so hard to clean up the area, it must certainly contain harmful substances. Once the process begins, it becomes almost impossible to convince knowledgeable lay people that they will not be harmed. The major accomplishment of Superfund was prospective. Industries creating toxic wastes could no longer dump them in or on the ground. Wastes have to be disposed of properly as they accumulate, and the expense is to the industry rather than to the taxpayer. Whether or not the process of Superfund will be modified to reduce this expense and effort is debatable. Anyone suggesting doing less is immediately criticized as being uncaring and unconcerned about the health of exposed people.

Proposition 65

As part of their efforts in participative democracy, California voters are permitted to initiate numerous referendums or propositions on the ballot at regularly scheduled elections. Although theoretically an improvement over representative government, this practice allows controversial and complex issues to be passed into law. In many instances, California is then encumbered by poorly conceived legislation, much of which becomes a major compromise to good government. Such an example is Proposition 65, enacted into law almost twenty years ago. The proposition decreed that any industrial discharge of substances capable of causing cancer or birth defects in any lab animal into drinking water would have to be made known by the manufacturer of the substance.[6]

The proposition had many glaring deficiencies. First, the quantitation of the offending substance was never clearly defined. Because of sophisticated assay technology, minute amounts of trace chemicals can be detected. Secondly, for many of the chemicals listed, no evidence was available to demonstrate harm to anyone in even a single case. Thirdly, the proposition did not distinguish between naturally occurring and man-made substances. One of the most objectionable features of Proposition 65 is the provision permitting any citizen to sue any business that the person believes is not following the law. This citizen suit provision has been described as the "bounty hunter" provision, requiring the defendant to show that a discharge of a substance was lawful, rather than the plaintiff having to show that it was unlawful. Finally, at trace levels of detection, almost none of the identified substances has had any human impact. Unfortunately, because the proposition mandated consumer warnings, the use of perfectly safe substances were compromised by lay anxiety.

Worst of all, the proposition left the public with the belief that industrial chemicals were responsible for cancer. The accepted truth is that such chemicals have a minimal or absent causation for human cancer. Lifestyle choices are far more important.

Indeed, Proposition 65 is absurd and of little or no value to the health and safety of Californians. The people would be far better off if they left such complex and important issues to their elected representatives.

Alar

We've covered this apple preservative earlier. Fortunately, reason has prevailed and we now benefit from the availability of an excellent food at modest cost. Alar does its job and is free of posing danger.

Saccharin and Cyclamates

The widely publicized ban on cyclamate sweeteners led to investigations of the carcinogenic potential of saccharin. Early studies of Canadian laboratory rodents fed huge doses of saccharin revealed a handful of bladder tumors in the rats.[7] The doses required in those studies would translate into a tank car full of sweetened soda pop in humans. Subsequent human studies did not demonstrate any risk of bladder or other cancer from either cyclamates or saccharin.[8] The extrapolation of animal tumors to human risk, not taking into account dose, duration of exposure, or toxicity thresholds, provides misleading information.

Again, this type of concern derives from the philosophy that a rodent is a "little human." This misguided thinking has spawned unprecedented increases in environmental legislation, ostensibly designed to protect us from cancer. All that is accomplished is increased cost of goods and services, high insurance and legal fees, and the reduction of job opportunities and of incentives for innovation. Fear of tort litigation deters entrepreneurial businesses from creating new and useful products. This occurs without the realization of any known public health benefit.

Medical Waste Tracking Act of 1988[9]

This legislation may represent the ultimate example of ludicrous activity. Although designed to protect the public from disease, the legislation ignored scientific reasons against adopting it offered by many scientific establishments. Public panic prevailed; the foolish legislation remains on the scene, contributing to the inflation of healthcare costs.

The legislation followed the discovery of used syringes and needles washed up on the beaches of the Atlantic seaboard. The public immediately presumed that this was caused by the careless disposal of medical wastes by healthcare facilities. A public panic ensued caused by the conviction that innocent people exposed to the discarded medical paraphernalia would succumb to serious viral diseases, notably hepatitis and AIDS. During the congressional hearings that preceded the enactment of the legislation, the CDC, the National Institutes of Health, and several infectious disease organizations testified that medical waste generated in legitimate healthcare facilities posed no hazard to anyone. The legislation would be of no value to public safety. It was later learned that the discarded needles and syringes came from drug addicts and diabetics, not healthcare facilities. Further, detailed epidemiologic studies never demonstrated a health hazard to hospital personnel, apart from the risk of being injured by sharp objects and needles. Workers in sanitary landfills have never incurred infections from their occupation. Despite the contrary evidence and testimony, public panic prevailed, and the legislation passed. The result is a ridiculous proliferation of expensive activity in healthcare facilities, none of which makes any difference. We are now compelled to separate medical waste from ordinary waste, bag medical waste separately, and engage in incineration disposal. These efforts cost five times as much as sanitary landfill disposal and accomplishes nothing. Limiting the process to careful disposal of sharp objects and needles would require special precautions for only 1 percent of hospital waste. As it is, we waste thousands of dollars annually on special disposal procedures, all of which entails unnecessary costs, and which contribute nothing to the safety of healthcare personnel or the public.

THE ENVIRONMENTAL MOVEMENT

Finally, let's discuss the sensitive subject of a small minority of the environmental movement that has created unnecessary concerns and anxiety in our population. The environmental movement has made great strides in protecting our air, water, forests, and lakes from readily demonstrable industrial pollution. Environmental organizations have made significant progress, and our general environment is far cleaner than it was during the latter half of the twentieth century. Despite continued industrialization of Western civilization, pollution of the general environment in the developed world is reasonably controlled. A small faction of the environmental movement, those often with an anti-business or anti-development political agenda, have decided that associating pollution with human disease is an effective way of achieving their goals. Understandably people are concerned about health issues, particularly cancer and birth defects. If the public can be convinced that any pollution of the environment is a health hazard, then the goals of this small minority are more readily achieved. Examples of their successes have already been covered: Superfund, California Proposition 65, The Delaney Clause, etc.

Although the environmentalists prefer to indict industrial and agricultural pollution as the major causes of human disease, my preference is to divide pollution into three categories: 1) general pollution affecting everyone; 2) occupational pollution hazards limited to specific workers and occupations; and 3) personal pollution. I shall attempt to demonstrate that general pollution is a minor factor; occupational pollution is predictable and controllable; and personal pollution is by far the most significant culprit in causing human disease.

General Pollution

Historically, general pollution has been incriminated in several serious health disasters. The notorious London smog of 1952 caused thousands of deaths in a few weeks. London always had impressive fog, often carrying acids from coal burned to generate electricity. The unusual climatic inversion of that period concentrated the acids. The majority of the reported coal-related deaths occurred in those with pre-existing chronic lung disease due to cigarette smoking. A half century ago, the majority of English people were smokers. The combination of pre-existing pulmonary disease, plus the presence of acids in the air, resulted in premature deaths. Since that time, major changes in electric power generation have pretty much cleaned up the air in London. The more recent visitors to London have noted the relative lack of fog and associated eye and lung irritations. Instead of burning coal, most efforts to generate power now use cleaner natural gas from the North Sea. Less impressive progress has occurred with the dry smog of Los Angeles and other cities, which is mostly attributed to automobile exhaust fumes.

Another serious example of general pollution occurred in Japan in the 1950s as a result of major industrial mercury pollution of the waters off the coast of Japan.[10] The mercury was initially consumed by fish, concentrating in fat, and was then introduced into the human food chain with disastrous results. Major neurological disorders, including deaths and paralysis, affected thousands of Japanese people. Experts identified the source of the oceanic pollution quickly, discontinued the dumping process, and solved the problem. The above examples of general pollution of the environment are real, readily identified and controlled, and far different from the vague notions of pollution and theoretical hazards which are widely publicized and become a source of unjustified anxiety in the public.

Other sources of general environmental pollution have achieved notoriety in the past several decades. Although the theoretical hazards of these pollutants have not materialized into human disease, the public panic and anxiety persists and unwarranted activity by government has occurred and persists.

CANCER CLUSTERS

Closely related to the belief that environmental pollution causes human disease is the concept of cancer clusters.[11] There is a wide disparity between public perceptions and scientific findings about this issue. Recent popular movies, such as *Erin Brockovich*, have reinforced the public belief that pollution causes disease. Although there are documented instances in which chemical exposure has caused cancers, most of the association between exposure and cancer cited in "clusters" are not supported by evidence. The major associations between exposure to chemicals and the occurrence of cancer have almost all involved occupational or lifestyle behaviors, such as cigarette smoking or alcohol abuse, and not larger scale events.

Definition

A cancer cluster refers to a geographic area, time period, or group of people with a greater than expected number of cases of cancer. Epidemiologists who investigate the causes and distribution of human diseases expect cancer rates to vary slightly from year to year and use statistical tests to determine whether a given cancer rate is different enough from average to qualify as an unexpected rate. Proving that a cancer cluster exists entails doing rigorous statistical analysis, in which the number of cases observed is compared with the expected number for that time period and area.

The claim that there is a "cancer cluster" typically derives from impressions of a few lay people who believe that their living area exhibits an unusually high incidence of cancer. These individuals then exert pressure upon responsible public officials to investigate the "cluster." If dissatisfied with the initial official response, these dedicated individuals may appeal to higher levels of government. The belief in the cluster often results in extensive and expensive epidemiologic studies. In almost every instance, the "cluster" is found to be epidemiologically without merit, but not before a great deal of money, time, and energy have been expended.

Clusters of cancer are a real phenomenon and have been statistically documented and explained. The few "real" cancer clusters serve as an example of how specific chemical exposures are capable of causing specific cancers, not vague combinations of health disorders.

Diethylstilbestrol (DES) was widely used in the 1940s and 1950s to prevent premature labor and first trimester spontaneous abortions (i.e., miscarriages). The medical reasoning was that the placenta produced insufficient amounts of estrogen (i.e., the female hormone) to support the pregnancy, a level that could be bolstered by DES. DES is a synthetic estrogen originally used to treat advanced prostate cancer in men. The action of the estrogen opposed androgen (i.e., the male sex hormone) production, the latter of which supported the growth of the cancer. Some fifteen years later, some astute Boston physicians noted that a hitherto very rare cancer—clear cell cancer of the vagina—was occurring with undue frequency in a large number of very young women. This rare cancer had been seen previously only in elderly women. They investigated the medical history of these young women and found that their mothers had all been treated with DES for threatened abortion. The DES hormonal effect apparently created an anomaly in the developing fetus which much later caused the vaginal cancer. This use of DES was then discouraged, and then banned by the FDA. The problem is now history and provides a concrete example of the possible specificity of a cancer cluster.

A second equally specific example of a cancer cluster, involving hepatic (liver) angiosarcoma, was identified in workers exposed to a precursor substance in the manufacture of vinyl materials. This very rare vascular cancer in the liver was caused by the specific chemical. Appropriate controls are now in place to protect workers from this substance.

Erin Brockovich

This popular movie, staring Julia Roberts in the title role, depicts the real life story of a class action litigation against a California utility. Brockovich was a paralegal working for a large plaintiff-oriented law firm. The utility was apparently responsible for contaminating the water supply of a small town with chromium-6, a chemical used to retard rust formation. Brockovich interviewed the eight hundred citizens of Hinkley and found that they suffered from a great variety of health problems, including nosebleeds, breast cancer, Hodgkin's disease, chronic fatigue syndrome, spontaneous abortions, spinal "deterioration," etc.

Although not a trained epidemiologist, Brockovich concluded that the number and types of disorders were excessive for that community. She further concluded that the chromium-6 drinking water contamination was responsible. Her law firm sued the utility and won a huge settlement (one-third of a billion dollars). The utility decided that the widespread negative publicity which they had been subjected to would make a fair jury trial impossible.

Chromium-6 is listed as a human carcinogen by the EPA, but it is problematic only when inhaled, not when consumed in drinking water. Further, studies of other communities in which chromium-6 was present in similar quantities in water revealed no increased incidence of any cancer.[12] In addition, exposed workers in the plants manufacturing chromium-6 demonstrated no increased incidence of cancer. Finally, studies of laboratory animals given huge doses of chromium-6 in their drinking water suffered no ill effects. Not only is there no evidence that chromium-6 had any adverse effect on Hinkley residents, but the notion that an environmental pollutant can cause such an extensive host of unrelated diseases is patently absurd. In addition to the injustice of the financial settlement is the anxiety evident in Hinkley residents, many of whom were convinced that they would suffer a host of diseases for the rest of their lives. So much for the justice of our tort litigation system. It remains justice for, by, and of the lawyers.

Breast Cancer in a Minnesota Suburb

Several decades ago a brief report by the Minnesota Department of Health described an increased incidence of breast cancer in women living in St. Louis Park (a Minneapolis suburb). This report coincided with the discovery that two of the city's deep wells were contaminated by creosote residue, undoubtedly because of the town's proximity to a long-abandoned creosote plant. Real estate sales declined in this suburb as a major concern about developing breast cancer spread. Affected wells were closed and subsequent analyses of water in St. Louis Park revealed no further contamination.

A later study by the Health Department revealed that St. Louis Park, a suburb with a 20 percent Jewish population, had an expected incidence of breast cancer, considering its ethnic make-up. Unfortunately, the clarification of the cause and effect was buried in the newspapers. Negative results, it seems, are insufficiently frightening and newsworthy.

Summary of Cancer Clusters

The study of "cancer clusters" may be the epitome of the ongoing battle between the forces of science versus anti-science. The latter "know" that their position is valid and ridicule the importance of scientific validation studies in evaluating controversial health issues. Evidence is required to evaluate alleged "cancer clusters." Without statistically controlled studies, people are afflicted with undue anxieties and all kinds of useless activities are generated to correct alleged pollution.

Dioxin

Dioxin is a powerful toxin, and an unfortunate and inadvertent byproduct of the manufacturer of certain herbicides. The first well-documented major exposure to dioxin was in Seveso, Italy. Contamination of this town resulted in human evacuation and permanent fencing-off of the area. Fortunately, the Italian public health people followed the evacuated families carefully. No increase in malignancies or birth defects has ever been demonstrated.

A second potential disaster occurred in Times Beach, Missouri, where large amounts of dioxin accidentally contaminated road paving material. The potential risk involved eight hundred families with twenty-four hundred people. When the error was identified, the area was evacuated and fenced in. After ten years of observation, experts have found no increase in cancer or birth defects. It is now concluded that dioxin contamination poses little or no harm to exposed persons.

A recent bit of sensational news involved the attempted assassination of a Ukrainian dissident political leader. He was secretly fed a large dose of dioxin. His sole medical problem was severe chloracne, a chronic and disfiguring skin condition known to be a result of exposure to dioxin. The Ukrainian leader was otherwise well; the skin condition was the only documented medical problem.

Perhaps the most widely publicized dioxin contamination occurred in Operation Ranch Hand during the Vietnam conflict. To eliminate the enemy's jungle cover, the Air Force dropped huge amounts of Agent Orange. Agent Orange was a standard defoliant, the production of which inadvertently created small amounts of dioxin. Many Air Force personnel were exposed to Agent Orange, creating a huge problem for the Veterans Administration. When the war ended, the returning veterans suffered from a variety of medical problems, the incidence of which was, however, expected in any population. Agent Orange and dioxin were incriminated by the veterans, resulting in a host of complex medical and epidemiologic studies. In repeated investigations, the incidence of malignancies in the exposed Vietnam Air Force veterans was found to be identical to any age-adjusted veteran population. The Center for Disease Control (CDC) compared dioxin levels in blood, urine, and fat of exposed veterans with those veterans who had never been to Vietnam. [13] The levels in the exposed and the non-exposed veterans were the same. Slight but significant increases in rare tumors have occurred in Vietnam veterans, though the incidences are no higher in those Air Force veterans with dioxin exposure than other military personnel. These small increases would be statistically expected in any epidemiologic study of the health of any group of people.

Nevertheless, the VA could not withstand the political pressure and gave financial compensation to any veteran with these rare cancers. Aside from the injustice of compensating veterans for conditions unrelated to their military service, the greater injustice has been to convince these exposed veterans that they are at risk for developing cancer or fathering three-headed children. I doubt that any financial compensation received will equal the anxiety which many veterans incurred from this association.

Since almost nothing adverse to health has been documented from these several dioxin spills (other than the recognized chloracne in the Ukrainian dissident) it becomes apparent that the risk of dioxin exposure is either miniscule or absent. More harm is done in terms of human anxiety than could ever occur from dioxin toxicity.

Love Canal

Although the Love Canal pollution debacle is now history, it provides another example of a theoretical health hazard caused by pollution without evidence of human disease. Hooker Chemical Company had an extensive chemical industry in western New York that operated during and shortly after World War II. Many potentially toxic chemicals were produced, including chlorinated organic substances and chemicals which caused dioxin production. As was the standard practice of the time, waste chemicals were disposed on or near the production plant, in this case in a clay-lined ditch named Love Canal. When Hooker discontinued their production, the land was sold to the local Board of Education for one dollar, the transfer deed cautioning against subsequent human habitation or other human use. The Board ignored the warning, built a school, and sold the rest of the property to a developer for home construction.

Some years later, odorous liquids seeped into the basements of several of the new homes. It was quickly learned that the toxic chemicals from Love Canal had contaminated the homes of the residents. The area was evacuated, the homes compensated for, and the area fenced in. Subsequent epidemiologic studies of the exposed families revealed no increase in cancer or birth defects. The history was further complicated by a genetics laboratory report that chromosomal breaks were found in many of the exposed individuals. Further investigation revealed that the information was false, and that the laboratory had been hired by an environmental group desiring to continue the debacle. Then Governor Cuomo convened a blue ribbon group to investigate all the claims and counterclaims. It concluded that no human harm had occurred.

Radiation Exposure

No one questions the potential for environmental disasters from nuclear energy production of electric power. The Chernobyl nuclear plant disaster contributed greatly to a continued fear of nuclear plants as a source of electricity generation. Unfortunately, the Ukrainian plant could in no way be compared to nuclear facilities in the Western democracies. Seventy percent of electric power in France is generated by nuclear energy, and without any accidents. The sole accident in the United States was at the Three Mile Island facility. Although causing immediate concern, it didn't result in any human harm. Whether or not this country will resume nuclear plant construction is a heated political issue.

The personal concern about radioactivity is raised repeatedly by the warning that radon gas seeping into basements can cause health problems. Cigarette manufacturers would love to incriminate this gas as the cause of lung cancer instead of cigarette smoking. Some twenty to thirty years ago, a radon scare resulted in radon monitoring of the basements of homes before they could be sold. Concern about radon periodically resurfaces. The only significant documented radon exposures have occurred in a seven county area on the border between New Jersey and Pennsylvania.[14] This area has a unique granite formation enabling more radon to seep to the surface, elevating radon concentrations in home basements. One study revealed a slight increase in lung cancer in this area. Evacuating air from basements with simple exhaust fans solved the problem. No other parts of the country appear to have a significant radon problem.

Most of our radioactivity exposure derives from cosmic radiation, and the degree of exposure exceeds any levels of radiation from medical diagnostic work or nuclear energy reactivity.

OCCUPATIONAL POLLUTION

Occupational disease is a major and important source of environmental pollution. Associated diseases are solely incurred by workers in specific industries. Perhaps the most significant occupational disorders over the past half century are those caused by the inhalation of asbestos fibers from a variety of manufactured products. Although mining of asbestos and the manufacture of asbestos-containing products are significant sources of exposure, the greatest incidence occurs in occupations in which the worker may be unaware that the product involved contained asbestos. And given its properties, asbestos is used in many products. Asbestos is essentially an inert mineral, with unique resistance to heat, acids, or any corrosive agent. It can be woven, cast, sprayed, or utilized in a variety of applications. Its incorporation into many products relates entirely to its low cost and physical qualities.

Thousands of cases of debilitating and fatal chronic pulmonary disease have resulted from occupational exposure to asbestos, often involving exposure from products workers did not know were risks. The magnificent work of Selikoff and associates linked asbestos occupational exposure to lung cancer and the rare pleural malignancy, mesothelioma.[15] It is widely recognized that asbestos disease is almost always associated with major occupational exposure. Casual exposure and household contacts are not a risk. Despite this knowledge, we are spending billions of dollars each year removing asbestos insulation from schools and public buildings. Suggestion has been made that the difficult removal process itself is a greater source of environmental contamination than leaving the insulation material undisturbed. Again, in this case public panic is fueled by environmentalists with little or no yield in public safety.

Now that knowledge of the hazard of asbestos in manufactured products is widely available, future occupational exposure should be minimal and controlled. The current overwhelming problem is compensation of exposed workers for the incurred disorders. Such compensation is thwarted by the combined efforts of plaintiff attorneys and labor unions. Class action suits have been instituted on behalf of exposed workers who lack apparent disease. Companies that have been sued include Johns Manville, Minnesota Mining and Manufacturing, and dozens of others. This expansion of litigation has served only to bankrupt some of the accused companies and to dilute compensation appropriate for workers with demonstrated disease. Again, the tort attorneys complicate justice.

PERSONAL ENVIRONMENTAL POLLUTION

The public and, unfortunately, many physicians who should know better, accept the proposition that pollution in the general environment is responsible for most cancers as well as a host of other diseases. In truth, pollution within the reach of one's hands causes most diseases. This personal environmental pollution has been attributed to lifestyle choices and consists of cigarette smoking, alcohol abuse, the American diet, sexual incontinence, and excessive sun exposure. The outstanding work of Doll and Peto from Oxford and other consensus conferences estimate that lifestyle practices are responsible for upwards of 85 percent of human cancers. [16] Occupational exposure possibly accounts for 4 percent of malignancies. The general group of environmental pollution exposure, food additives, medical and drug exposures, etc., account for no more than 10 percent of all cancers.

Some of the evidence of the role of personal pollution in human disease is incontrovertible fact; some is epidemiological. The prime role of cigarette smoking is directly responsible for 450,000 excess deaths in this country each year. Smoking kills by causing cancer, chronic pulmonary disease, and increased cardiovascular disease. Excessive alcohol consumption accounts for one hundred thousand deaths. Alcohol and cigarettes synergistically account for the majority of upper respiratory and upper gastrointestinal tract cancers.

The epidemiological evidence linking major cancers with the American diet is overwhelming. Cancers of the breast, endometrium, colon, and prostate are linked to saturated fat consumption. Differences in cancer incidence between the developed world and Third World nations directly correlate with saturated fat consumption. Contributing to this epidemiological evidence is data from cancer incidences in migrating populations and changes within a nation with time. Japanese migrants to Hawaii and California leave behind the low breast and colon cancer incidence of Japan and assume the high incidence of these conditions that Americans display in just one or two generations. The incidence of breast cancer in Japan dramatically increased with the Americanization of their diet. Japanese girls are now taller and heavier and menstruate earlier, changes proportional to the increase in breast cancer in Japanese women.

SUMMARY

There is widespread public belief that general pollution of the environment by industrial and agricultural practices is responsible for the majority of human diseases, notably cancer and birth defects. I find this almost universal conclusion a mystery, since the facts prove otherwise. Despite the fact that much of the twentieth century has witnessed tremendous levels of environmental pollution, the incidence and mortality of cancer has not changed. If a relationship existed, one would reasonably expect a major increase in cancer. Further, despite the increasing level of pollution, the incidence of birth defects has remained constant at 5 percent. Again, if pollution causes birth defects, many more birth defects would have occurred.

Three elements of our society are largely responsible for this pervasive misinformation: the media, government, and a handful of environmental "apocalyptics." The media distorts the truth because frightening news or sensational exposés sell newspapers and television time. Governmental institutions enact poorly conceived legislation, in part because the laws do not require much federal financing and in part because elected officials curry favor with the voters. A small group of environmentalists, though not those responsible for our successes in cleaning up the air and waters, hope that linking pollution with disease will enhance their anti-business and anti-development agendas. Study after study has demonstrated that the implication of pollution of the environment in human disease is a relatively rare occurrence. As was demonstrated earlier in our discussion of cancer, most cancers are caused by lifestyle factors.

Occupational pollution is real, but generally readily demonstrated and controlled. Cancer "clusters" occur but are very specific in terms of causes and diseases created. When epidemiologically studied, the reputed "clusters" are found to be no more common than statistically expected.

References

1. J. C. Bailar and E. M. Smith, "Progress Against Cancer?" *N Eng J Med* 314, No 19 (May 8, 1986): (1226-32).

2. F. A. Marshall, "A is for Apple, Alar, and Alarmist," *Science* 254, No 5028 (Oct 4, 1991): 20-2.

3. CBS, *Face to Face with Connie Chung*: (Dec 10, 1990).

4. M. Angell, "Evaluating the Health Risks of Breast Implants," *New Eng J Med* No. 334, 23, (June 6, 1996): 1513-18.

5. E. L. Johnson, "Nature, Extent, and Impact of Superfund Hazardous Waste Sites," *Chemosphere* 31 (1995): 12415-28.

6. D. R. Juberg, "California's Proposition 65 and Its Impact on Public Health," *Am Council on Science and Health* (December 2000): http://www.acsh.org/publications/pubID.146/pub_detail.asp

7. J. M. Price, et al, "Bladder Tumors in Rats Fed a Mixture of Cyclamate and Saccharin," *Science* 1970; 1967: 1131-2.

8. F. Cordle and S. A. Miller. "Using Epidemiology to Regulate Food Additives," *Public Health Reports* 99, 4 (1984): 365-9.

9. W. A. Ratala and D. J. Weber "Infectious Waste - Mismatch Between Science and Policy," *New Eng J Med* 325, (August 22, 1991): 578-82.

10. T. Luchino, et al, "Neurologic Features of Chronic Organic Mercury Poisoning," *J Environ Sci Health* 30, No 5, (1995): 699-711.

11. G. G. Caldwell, "Twenty-Two Years of Cancer Cluster Investigation at the CDC," *Am J Epic* 132, (1990): 543-47.

12. M. Fumento, "Erin Brockovich Exposed," *The Wall St J* Vol 235, Issue 62(March 28, 2000): A30

13. Centers for Disease Control, "Serum Dioxin Levels in US Army Vietnam-Era Veterans," *JAMA* 20, No 9, (September 2, 1988): 124-54.

14. B. L. Cohen, "Association of Lung Cancer Mortality With the Precambrian Granite of the Reading Prong," *Arch Environ Health* 43 No. 4, (Jul-Aug 1988): 313-5

15. J. Selikoff, J. Churg, E. C. and Hammond, "Asbestos Exposure and Neoplastia," *JAMA* 188, (1964): 22-26.

16. R. Doll and R. Peto, "The Causes of Cancer: Quantitative Estimates of Avoidable Risks of Each in the Cancer in the U.S.," *J Nat Cancer Inst* 66, (1981): 1191.

6

Are Dietary Supplements Necessary?

Although the lay public may not view dietary supplements as "necessary," over 80 percent of our citizens consume supplements.[1] This heavy consumption of hundreds or thousands of products mandates some explanation. After all, many people never consume any supplements, and yet appear and apparently are healthy. Those who regularly ingest one or more supplements should recognize that many of their fellow citizens do not use supplements and yet are not ill. Why, given this clear fact, is consumption of dietary supplements so commonplace? I am reminded of an experience of my daughters, who baby-sat many years ago for an Amway salesperson. The children of this Amway representative consumed all kinds of vitamin supplements, which were kept in a bowl on the kitchen table. Of course, my daughters did not consume any vitamin preparations of any kind. Somehow the Amway children were not surprised that my healthy daughters did not take vitamin pills, and yet the Amway family continued to do so. This family didn't seem bothered by this apparent contradiction.

Many lay persons believe that physicians are both disinterested in and know little about nutrition. Their personal physician may have never discussed nutrition with them, other than its relation to the problems of obesity. Their physician may have very rarely recommended or endorsed the use of vitamin pills, protein supplements, or herbal preparations. Perhaps patients review this lack of comment by physicians as both lack of knowledge and interest. As a result, lay people may heed the intense marketing of supplements as factual, and believe that their health and well-being will be enhanced by consuming supplements.

This apparent lack of interest in supplements by physicians may have a simple explanation. Their "disinterest" may be a rational reflection of the fact that physicians rarely or never encounter nutritional deficiency of any kind in their everyday medical practice. How often do physicians see cases of scurvy (vitamin C lack), beri beri and pellagra (B vitamin lack), or protein deficiency? I would venture that the majority of physicians never see a documented case of such vitamin and nutritional deficiency in their entire practice lifetimes. And so we should ask, "Why would physicians maintain an interest in clinical problems they never encounter?" Physicians who watch television must be amused at the advertising for Ensure, a protein supplement. Depicted is an attractive couple, both people in their middle years, actively enjoying the good life. The assumption is that they have the good life because they regularly consume Ensure. But such vigor and health surely can not result from consuming a protein supplement. And yet a lot of Ensure is consumed. Purveyors of such products are as successful as the snake oil salesman of an earlier era. Perhaps the "disinterested" physicians are smarter than their patients believe.

Vitamin and other nutritional deficiencies do occur, particularly in Third World nations where starvation and malnutrition are widespread. People who subsist on five hundred calories per day of ground corn and nothing else would be expected to have deficiencies. The major comparable condition in the developed world is chronic alcoholism, which can be systematically devastating. Yet even most alcoholics eat enough to avoid deficiencies. By no stretch of the imagination can Third World dietary conditions be compared with the dietary abundance and variety in the developed world.

Many people also seem to believe that they know more about nutrition than their physician. The reason they hold this belief is clear. Print and visual media bombard the public with nutrition product advertising. And this information is propagated by marketing people with a profit motive. Unfortunately, lay people are relatively gullible about these promotions, often believing that what they hear or see *must* be true. After all, the companies promoting these nutrition products would not lie. Or would they? Of course they can and they do, because there are no legal proscriptions against nutrition product hucksterism. The federal government has essentially zero control over supplement promotion. Purveyors of these products make any claim they want, and the public accepts a significant amount of this misinformation as fact. The vendors of supplements successfully follow the teaching of Joseph Goebbels, Hitler's propaganda chief: "The bigger the lie, the more it is believed." The lack of any control over vendor claims will be covered later in this section. Unfortunately, most consumers don't know about the absence of any promotion control.

Indeed, most physicians do not see nutritional deficiency in their practice. If deficiency disorders do not occur, why would physicians give them any attention? Hypernutrition on the other hand, resulting in our increasingly overweight population, is a daily issue in clinical practice. The purveyors of supplements have an answer to this observation. They point out that, although a person may be obese, the excess fat is due to eating the wrong foods. The diet may be deficient in specific nutrients. Support for this position, of course, is unavailable. Even junk food, high in calories and saturated fats, contains abundant vitamins, minerals, and protein.

Another effective marketing ploy of supplement vendors is claiming that the consumption of dietary supplements creates a condition of "superior" health. It would be nice to see some evidence. Unfortunately, evidence is not always very important to the lay public. People generally accept hucksterism as fact because it "makes sense." However, what "makes sense" ought to be what withstands the scrutiny of scientific validation. The purveyors of supplements ridicule this requirement as a "scientific hang-up." They "know" that their product has value in improving health. Repeatedly, when supplements are scientifically evaluated for efficacy, however, almost all are found to be without value. The sole benefit is to the bottom line of the purveyor.

The classical example of remunerative hucksterism took place decades ago in the Deep South. Hadacol, a multivitamin preparation in a 20 percent, flavored alcohol solution, was widely sold to teetotaling Baptists as a nutritional supplement. The good people understandably believed that if one tablespoon was good, several were better. Indeed, when they drank several ounces of Hadacol, they did feel better; the "benefit" was from the alcohol. The preparation was very similar to port wine.

An ongoing debate about food supplements attempts to determine if nutrients are more effectively consumed in a balanced diet or as nutrition supplements. There is growing support for the belief that foods contain vital nutrients not yet identified that contribute to health. These nutrition factors are of course not found in supplements because their exact nature is not known. Nutrient factors in foods are never present in toxic quantities, though they may be in certain supplements. Increasingly, nutritionists are coming to the conclusion that people should get their nutrition factors from food rather than commercial pills.

VITAMINS

Taking a daily multivitamin pill is widely accepted by the lay public as beneficial to good health. The pills are inexpensive and the quantities of vitamins they contain are safe. Economy and safety do not address the basic question of need, however. Do people require or benefit from a daily multivitamin preparation? The safety aspect does not apply to megavitamin preparations (i.e., therapeutic doses) containing large quantities, and often including fat-soluble vitamins with toxicity potential. Cases of hypervitaminosis have been caused by "therapeutic" vitamin D pills, involving serious kidney and bone problems. More important than the potential for toxicity with fat-soluble megavitamins is the basic question, what is being treated with "therapeutic" vitamins? Vitamin requirements are well established and are readily satisfied with the low doses present in everyday multivitamin pills. Water-soluble vitamins (such as C and B vitamins) are excreted in the urine when ingested beyond the body's needs. Giving "therapeutic" amounts accomplishes little more than more renal (kidney) excretion.

In part, multivitamins are so successfully sold because of the unrealistic requirements listed as minimal daily requirements (MDRs). Do we really need 40 – 60 milligrams of ascorbic acid (vitamin C) each day to prevent a deficiency? Vitamin C deficiency in the diet was a real problem to the British Navy two hundred years ago. Sailors who were at sea for months had a diet completely lacking fresh fruits or vegetables. Their diet included only salted meat and grains which would not spoil during lengthy sea voyages. They essentially had no vitamin C in their diet. Surprisingly, not everybody on these voyages suffered from vitamin C deficiency. The discovery that a small amount of lemon juice would prevent scurvy was a godsend to the sailors (though if British sailors consumed lemons to prevent scurvy, why are they called "Limeys?"). The amount adequate to prevent vitamin C deficiency might be as little as 1 or 2 milligrams per day, far less than our recommended MDR of 60 milligrams.

We can think similarly about our dietary protein requirement. One recommendation is that we should consume 70 grams of protein daily to ensure good health. However, individuals consuming far less because of absorption disorders or strange dietary practices rarely show signs of protein deficiency.

All of the above should not leave the reader with the impression that consuming a multivitamin pill daily is unwise. If you think it makes you better, feel free to continue. I personally do not use vitamin preparations and my health is about as good as anyone my age.

ANTIOXIDANTS

A scientific "rage" of recent times is believing that certain antioxidants prevent cancer and heart disease. This widespread belief derived from animal studies and poorly designed clinical trials over ten years ago. The value of antioxidants theoretically resulted from reducing oxidation of low-density lipoproteins, the causative mechanism of athero-sclerosis (i.e., hardening of the arteries). The theory led to recommendations to consume large amounts of antioxidants, particu-larly vitamin C, E, and beta carotene, a variant of vitamin A. Similarly antioxidants were thought to allegedly prevent cancer. They "made sense," and for several years, many authorities recommended consuming antioxidant vitamins.

However, as I have pointed out repeatedly, what "makes sense" must endure the scrutiny of controlled clinical trials. The trials have now been accomplished, demonstrating that antioxidant vitamins have no role in preventing atherosclerosis or cancer. The recently concluded Women's Health Study of forty thousand women (mostly nurses) revealed no benefit to vitamin E consumption.[2] A comparable study in men reveal that vitamin E does not prevent heart disease or cancer.[3]

The US Preventive Services Task Force (USPSFT) has officially stated not only do these vitamins lack any preventive function, but there is serious concern that the use of beta carotene for smokers actu-ally increases the incidence of lung cancer. Again, the notion that "it makes sense" falls victim to statistically valid clinical trials. Smokers incur enough risk for lung cancer without misguided "science" recom-mending an additional risk.

HERBAL SUPPLEMENTS

There is a widespread belief that, because herbal supplements are "natural" and generally derive from plants, they are safe. The belief stems from the notion that supplements are relatively inactive compared to prescription drugs. However, many herbal supplements have biologi-cal activity. This fact shouldn't be surprising. After all, in an earlier time, before modern pharmacology, most dispensed medications such as aspi-rin, morphine, quinine, and digitalis, were extracts of plants.

Digitalis

Perhaps the most classic example of a potent drug derived from a plant is digitalis. Older physicians may recall prescribing digitalis leaf tablets for their patients with congestive heart failure. The tablets were made of extracts of the leaf of the poisonous foxglove plant, *Digitalis purpurea*. The leaf was pulverized, the important compound extracted with a solvent, and then formed into a tablet. This was not an ideal process. The extraction process was relatively crude, undoubtedly recovering substances in addition to digitalis. A larger problem was the lack of uniformity of the extraction process; dispensed tablets often contained significantly more or less digitalis than presumed. This lack clearly led to increased variability in therapeutic effect. Current digitalis therapy uses chemical production of one or more pure digitalis preparations with precisely controlled constituents.

The history of digitalis therapy dates back over two hundred years ago, to the medical practice of Dr. William Withering, an English physician. One of his patients was a house-bound young woman, upon whom Dr. Withering regularly called in his practice. This young woman, afflicted with some poorly described malady, busied herself with watercolor paintings of flowers. Dr. Withering and his patient fell in love and were married. Dr. Withering frequently gathered plants and flowers for his wife's hobby. In his rounds of the countryside, he came upon a "healer" who used a secret herbal recipe derived from extracts of the poisonous foxglove plant. This "healer" had been dispensing extracts of *Digitalis purpurea* leaves for patients afflicted with dropsy, an old condition referring to the lower extremity edema of congestive heart failure.

In addition to providing the plant for his new wife's art work, the good doctor experimented with extracts of *Digitalis purpurea*. He made serial dilutions of an extract, and administered the drug in several forms and dosages to his patients with dropsy. His careful work achieved notable success with many patients and his reputation for digitalis therapy became known. Unfortunately, many of his fellow physicians did not follow Dr. Withering's careful methods. Some followed the belief that if some is good, more is better. As a result, digitalis toxicity became rampant, and many patients died. The scientific knowledge of the narrow therapeutic range of therapy of digitalis was not gained until many years later.

The example of the problems inherent in the preparation of digitalis extracts are compounded in many dispensed herbal supplements. Often the extraction techniques are relatively crude, resulting in extraction of substances from the plants other than the desired product. Further, the technique cannot always guarantee a level of constituent control: some supplement preparations may contain almost none of the alleged active ingredients while other extracts may contain much more than described. A recent study evaluated the chemical concentration of two widely-sold ginseng preparations. [4] The active ginseng ingredient varied from 10 percent to 300 percent of the stated concentration. This complete lack of control of potency is inherent in the extraction technology of most herbal supplements, probably accounting for lack of efficacy or toxicity. Prescription drugs whose manufacture is under the control of the FDA, are required to contain active ingredients in concentrations within plus or minus 10 percent of the stated dose.

This lack of manufacturing control of herbal supplements is due to lack of any governmental requirement of quality.

DSHEA

Background

The Dietary Supplement Health Education Act (DSHEA) was enacted by Congress in 1994 and signed into law by President Clinton. [5] This legislation was a successful response to a massive lobbying effort by the herbal supplement industry, with significant support by Senator Orrin Hatch, a ranking committee chairperson who is from Utah, a state with an inordinate number of dietary supplement manufacturers. The lobbyists convinced Congress that supplements were safe and that their availability was an example of consumerism in action, and the lobbyists supported the impression that physicians did not have enough knowledge about nutrition. In other words, they reinforced the lay public's belief that their physicians were ignorant about the subject. This legislation passed congressional scrutiny as easily as if it were about motherhood, the flag, and apple pie. The prior limited control by the FDA over dietary supplements was further limited. The FDA was essentially removed from controlling supplement manufacturing and promotion; the sole permitted activity remaining was overseeing preparation safety by a very inefficient reporting mechanism.

Since the DSHEA became law, companies have been able to say nearly anything they want about the potential health benefits of what they sell. As long as they don't blatantly lie or claim to have a cure for specific diseases, such as cancer, diabetes, or AIDS, they can state—without providing evidence—that a product is designed to support a healthy heart, protect cells from damage, or improve the function of a compromised immune system. There are almost no standards that regulate how the pills are made, and they receive almost no scrutiny once produced. Consumers never truly know what they are getting. Companies are not required to prove that products are effective, or even safe, before they are put on the market.

In addition to removing almost all governmental control over the manufacture and promotion of herbal supplements, the legislation contained a variety of vague and voluntary recommendations for the manufacturers. Their purveyors were told to utilize standardized extraction technique; but the techniques were not spelled out. The legislation recommended that manufacturers "should" work with competent medical researchers to assure safety and efficacy. The recommendations did not require compliance and companies rarely or never fulfilled them. Manufacturers claim that such research is too expensive to carry out. In other words, safety and efficacy claims are completely unfounded. If anything, we seem to be guaranteed that research will not be performed. Such research might reveal that the products sold are neither safe nor effective, findings that would be adverse to robust sales.

Comparing the requirements regulating the manufacture and sale of supplements with those of prescription drugs might prove revealing.

1. Prescription drugs are subject to rigorous controls of purity, stability, and lot-to-lot constituency. Supplements are subject to only vague recommendations for filth control and identity in the manufacture process.

2. Prescription drugs go through an intense safety and efficacy evaluation process prior to sale. Herbal supplement production has no such requirements.

3. Prescription drugs are approved for only a particular "intended use." Supplements have no particular use requirements and are sold to anyone who will purchase them.

4. Prescription drugs are developed and sold to treat specific disease conditions. Supplements may not be advertised for specific diseases. Claims of supplements are limited to general and vague descriptions, such as "improve energy," "enhance immunity," "increase well-being," "helps you relax," etc. Unfortunately, as is evident from the practices of health stores vending supplements, people are nevertheless advised to use this or that supplement for very specific disease problems, sometimes with disastrous results.

Negative Features of Supplements

When visiting their doctors, many people do not report their use of supplements. A Mayo study revealed that half of patients did not mention the use of supplements to their physician during visits. [6] Patients may believe innocently that the supplement they have been using is innocuous and could not affect their health adversely or influence any health problems they might have. After all, supplements are derived from plants and are therefore "natural" and safe. The potential harm of supplements is not appreciated by lay people. Some patients are too embarrassed to tell their physician that they tried a supplement for their current problem.

Patients and physicians don't always appreciate the potential adverse effects of taking supplements together with prescription drugs. For example, the widely consumed vitamin E preparations potentiate the effect of warfarin (an anticoagulant), potentially causing severe bleeding.

Or consider the effect of St. John's Wort on drug metabolism.[7] This supplement induces the production of a cytochrome enzyme system in the liver that enhances the metabolism of various drugs, both prescription and over-the-counter. This enhancement reduces the concentration and effectiveness of prescribed drugs, a result not widely appreciated. For example, plasma concentrations of alprazolam, a psychopharmacology preparation, are dramatically reduced in patients also taking St. John's Wort.

Ephedrine

The tragedies caused by ephedrine (Ephedra), found in many supplement preparations, has achieved sufficient notoriety.[8] Ephedrine-containing preparations are widely advertised for weight control and athletic performance enhancement. Ephedrine is contained in a great variety of health food preparations, often without being identified on the label. Although studies have not supported the effectiveness of ephedrine-containing preparations in weight reduction or improved athletic performance, these preparations are widely consumed because of fraudulent promotion.

Ephedra, which stimulates the central nervous system, is similar to amphetamines in chemical structure. It increases the heart rate and blood pressure. When combined with caffeine, as is often the case with weight-loss preparations, Ephedra magnifies these cardiovascular effects. Thousands of adverse effects, including dozens of deaths, have been reported. Because of the reported adverse effects, the FDA was permitted to ban Ephedra from many supplement products. Since Ephedra-containing preparations have been so successful economically, this reasonable FDA action is being challenged in the courts. This limited regulatory authority of the FDA of protecting the public is thus threatened. Furthermore, the reporting of adverse effects of any drug is inherently inefficient. First, the effect may not be recognized as due to the offending drug. Secondly, most clinicians elect to not be involved in regulatory activities affecting their patients.

SELECTED HERBAL SUPPLEMENTS

This section will cover only the more commonly sold herbal supplements, particularly the few which have been adequately studied for safety and efficacy.

Kava is a tranquilizing preparation widely used in Germany and other western European nations. Kava is alleged to be "relaxing," and is regarded as an alternative to prescribed antianxiety medications. At best, it is only mildly calming. However, numerous cases of severe liver toxicity currently being further evaluated by the FDA have been reported[9].

Shark Cartilage consumption was widely touted as a way to prevent cancer. Sharks allegedly do not get cancers and the purpose of the preparations was to confer this "cancer-prevention" property to humans. Unfortunately, the purpose has been unfulfilled. A controlled study revealed that cancers occurred at the same incidence in people taking shark cartilage preparations as in a control population. [10] Though ineffective, at least the preparation was safe.

Garlic was supposed to lower blood pressure and serum cholesterol. When studied in hypertensive and hypercholesterolemic patients, it lowered neither blood pressure nor cholesterol. I had thought that garlic was abandoned as a supplement, but I have noted recent advertisements on television hawking a garlic preparation.

Ginseng is widely used in the Far East for a variety of purposes. It allegedly "boosts" the heart, increases energy, and most importantly, acts as an aphrodisiac. Several controlled studies measuring oxygen consumption have revealed no energy improvement. It also fails to improve mood or cognition. Its effect on libido is too subjective to evaluate. The most obvious benefit is to Wisconsin farmers who grow ginseng plants for export.

Ginkgo biloba was widely promoted as a cerebral stimulant, and is widely consumed in the Far East. A controlled study did not support the manufacturer's claim of improved learning capacity and memory over a six-week study period.[10] Other claims of improved circulation and antioxidant activity were also unsupported. In studies of Alzheimer's patients, there was very slight slowing in the progress of the disease. Healthy people had no measurable cognitive improvement.

Echinacea is a widely used herbal product in Europe and the United States, allegedly effective against the common cold and other respiratory infections. Although widely accepted as "effective," almost all of the proponents were marketers of several echinacea products. A recent article in the *New England Journal of Medicine* described a University of Virginia study that investigated its purported value. [11] Volunteers were exposed to a particular rhinovirus known to cause the common cold in non-immune individuals. Half received echinacea extracted from a root in several dosages and over various periods of time. The other half received a placebo on a similar schedule. The incidence of the common cold and the severity and duration of symptoms were identical in both groups. This study may have been the first time that echinacea was administered in a predictable concentration. Purveyors of echinacea and several supplement trade organizations immediately attacked the study, claiming it used insufficient quantities of the supplement. This challenge ignores the fact that studies of echinacea use from several commercial preparations showed either no active ingredient or concentrations much higher than stated.

Hyaluronic acid is another widely promoted preparation, one useful in the therapy of knee osteoarthritis in intra-articular injection. Hyaluronic acid is a naturally occurring component of synovial fluid that probably contributes to joint lubrication. Because the therapy "made sense" and had no apparent adverse effects, the FDA approved hyaluronic acid for intra-articular use. As is so often the case, the practice greatly increased, at least until investigators subjected the therapy to a double-blind evaluation study.[12] The test group received intra-articular hyaluronic acid; the control group only a placebo. The groups had identical relief of pain and improved function, indicating that the benefits of the treatment were purely a placebo effect. Of course it would have been better to do the study before millions of dollars of useless therapy had been administered, but better late than never.

It is becoming increasingly clear that the supplement manufacturers do not want expansion of evaluation of their products for safety and efficacy. The studies thus far have failed to demonstrate value in many highly utilized and touted preparations.

THE FUTURE OF DIETARY SUPPLEMENTS

As long as the political powers in Congress hold sway, it is unlikely that DSHEA will be retracted. The notion that dietary supplements are safe because they are "natural" and usually derived from plants is utter nonsense. Supplements *are* biologically active, but in ways that have not been adequately documented. The existing legislation has essentially demonstrated that the FDA must retain control over the manufacture and sale of supplements. The very least the government should do is to demonstrate the safety and efficacy of supplements.[13] Without any controls, we are left with the hucksterism of a snake oil salesman of yesteryear.

The public deserves and requires the scrutiny of supplements by the FDA, along with appropriate oversight and evaluation in manners similar to that of prescription drugs. The notion that an uninformed consumer is capable of making sound, let alone scientific, judgments about the safety and efficacy of a marketed supplement is patently absurd. Before more disasters like those linked to Ephedra occur, the FDA should be given jurisdiction over the production and marketing dietary supplements. Entrepreneurial hucksters should not continue to market supplements without any safety and efficacy requirements.

DIRECT-TO-CONSUMER (DTC) ADVERTISING

It might be suggested that my reservations about the dietary supplement industry are excessive and biased. To address that criticism, I will attempt to demonstrate that the prescription drug industry is equally capable of nefarious activity. One particularly objectionable action of the pharmaceutical industry is direct-to-consumer advertising, a recent expansion of drug promotion designed to increase drug consumption.

The Food and Drug Administration (FDA) relaxed existing regulations governing direct-to-consumer (DTC) marketing in 1997. The pharmaceutical industry soon realized considerable financial gains from DTC marketing of several groups of prescription drugs. We should question the value of this change to our patients, both in terms of health and the problem of healthcare cost inflation.

The occurrence of DTC marketing, particularly on television, tripled in volume and expenditures during the first five years following the FDA regulation change. The marketing primarily involved pharmaceuticals utilized for chronic conditions and which are prescribed in large numbers. The most common groups include NSAIDs, a variety of preparations (such as proton pump inhibitors) used to combat gastric acidity, antihistamines lacking in drowsiness propensity, anti-lipidemics, antidepressants, and the new drugs used for erectile dysfunction. The selection of these particular groups was hardly an accident. These prescription items represent high-volume prescribing and drugs with a large price markup.

The increased sales of prescriptions has been impressive. DTC advertising works and the need to promote new drug preparations to physicians is both understandable and necessary. Developing new families of drugs is a very expensive venture. Hundreds of preparations are abandoned after expensive research endeavors because they prove to be either unsafe or lacking in efficacy. The rare success stories represent huge investment by the pharmaceutical industry and must achieve reasonably high usage to justify the development costs. Up until the recent relaxation of the FDA rules on DTC advertising, companies were limited to advertising in medical journals, physician mailings, and direct contact with "detail men" (i.e., pharmaceutical representatives). An unfortunate aspect of these earlier promotion techniques was a tendency to overstate the value and minimize the adverse effects of a particular preparation and so distortions of the truth are not limited to DTC advertising. And yet these earlier promotion methods had less effect on drug sales than DTC promotion. Recent data suggests that as many as 70 percent of drug-prescribing decisions derive in some part to DTC drug promotion. The busy practitioner, either simply to curry favor with the patient or simply to get the pressure off his or her proverbial back, may succumb to pressure and write the prescriptions that patients demand.

One classical example of the misleading DTC promotion involves the product Lamisil, intended for dermatomycosis of the toenails. This condition is an extremely common chronic infection of the toenail beds that creates discoloration. It endures for years without obvious effects on the patient other than aesthetic. The pharmaceutical company describes it as an "infection," a word used to create the impression of potential harm. Although the fungus disorder is indeed an "infection," it is most indolent and rarely requires therapy. In particular, taking an oral antimicrobial drug for months to eliminate the "infection" is gross over-treatment of an unimportant disorder. Consumers may spend hundreds or thousands of dollars on a non-disease. And Lamisil probably achieves significant sales, to the credit of DTC advertising.

Why did the FDA relax prevailing rules proscribing DTC advertising? Perhaps for the same reasons that the FDA lost jurisdiction over safety and efficacy of herbal supplements. Consumerism and choice have become public bywords. Industry lobbying has been eminently successful in persuading lawmakers that consumers have the right to make personal decisions affecting their health. The industry has been effective in convincing government and the lay public that the sole goal is to educate the citizens by providing them with information to take to their physicians.

Unfortunately, what is described as "education" by the pharmaceutical industry in DTC promotion is anything but education. The purpose of DTC advertising for the drug companies is a bottom line motivation to increase the volume of sales and hence profits. On the other hand, the purpose of education is the promotion of truth, which is rarely or very rarely a consideration in advertising. If anything, the real truth is intentionally distorted in advertising. The widespread use of testimonials for a product is an undisguised practice of implying good results for the promoted product. The possibility of lack of efficacy is rarely mentioned. (It's always, "This product will make you well.") Potential adverse side effects are mentioned, but they are generally minimized.

A particularly nefarious example of DTC advertising involves the replacement of a proton pump inhibitor preparation which had lost patent protection by a closely related preparation made by the same company. The older drug, although effective in doing what was claimed, is now an over-the-counter product. The new prescription drug, a minor molecular variant of the original, widely promoted as the "purple pill" (i.e., Nexium), is probably no more effective, but perhaps four to five times as expensive. Somehow millions of dollars of TV advertising for the "purple pill" are needed to achieve sufficient sales volume. Making matters worse is the anecdotal suggestion that the "purple pill" could be used to prevent dyspepsia in patients made uncomfortable when digesting certain foods. Instead of taking an expensive pill, the far wiser consumer decision would be to avoid these particular foods.

The most recent problem of DTC advertising, involving serious cardiovascular events caused by COX-2 inhibitors, has created a public panic. The older traditional NSAIDs—ibuprofen, acetaminophen, and naproxen—that are sold over-the-counter may be equal in efficacy to the highly promoted COX-2 inhibitors. The sole advantage of the latter is that they cause less gastrointestinal side effects in a small percentage of patients. Ideally, the COX-2 inhibitors would only be prescribed for a small number of patients sufficiently infrequently that the pharmaceutical companies would not resort to DTC advertising. Recognizing the few patients at risk for GI toxicity of traditional NSAIDs is easy; clinical guidelines are available. Patients at risk are those with advanced age, rheumatoid arthritis, warfarin and corticosteroid use, GI bleeding or ulcer, and GI symptoms with traditional NSAID use. Patients with those factors are considered "high risk" and should receive COX-2 inhibitors; others should not.

Another interesting feature of DTC advertising is that it is almost entirely an American phenomenon. New Zealand and the United States are the only developed countries that permit direct to consumer advertising for prescription drugs. Since all the medical schools in New Zealand have unanimously proposed a ban on DTC advertising, the United States may be alone in this very questionable practice.

Why has the FDA not been able to prevent these problems with their evaluation and approval of new drug preparations? The FDA is in a quandary. A few years ago, the agency was roundly criticized for being too slow in evaluation and approval of new drugs. Potential consumers complained loudly that drugs approved and widely used in Europe were unavailable to Americans. The FDA was being very conservative, hoping to avoid another thalidomide disaster. Reacting to the criticism, the FDA shortened its approval process. We may now be reaping the harvest of this decision. The drug approval process is very difficult. Randomized clinical trials adequately test short-term safety and efficacy of a new drug, at least as compared to controls. Unfortunately, such trials are of relatively small dimension and duration to be able to detect uncommon but clinically important or late adverse effects. Such appears to be the case with COX-2 inhibitors. Another problem of standard FDA drug evaluation is that patients with multiple co-morbid illnesses or those taking multiple medications are rarely included in their studies. If they were, the cost and time delay for drug approval might well be prohibitive.

The relaxation of FDA control on DTC marketing, although possibly well intentioned, was probably a political error and the result of paying too much attention to skillful lobbyists and insufficient attention to practicing physicians. Most physicians would welcome less drug promotion. Patient pressure for drug preparations promoted by DTC marketing is an added and onerous patient care demand. A far better goal in pharmacology would be the reduction of prescription drug usage. Patients would do as well or better, and part of our growing healthcare financing problems would be addressed successfully.

SUMMARY

The use of dietary supplements by the lay public has created a huge industry, but there is little scientific evidence to support the business. Part of the reason for consumer demand, despite the fact that most physicians rarely recommend the use of supplements, is a lay belief that physicians are neither interested in nor informed about supplements.

The most likely explanation about apparent physician "disinterest" is that physicians rarely see nutritional deficiencies in their patients. The real problem, finally receiving public attention, is hypernutrition, a condition resulting in our obesity epidemic.

Because of the almost complete lack of federal government control over supplements, the purveyors are free to make any and all claims about efficacy and safety. This absence of control stems from the Dietary Supplement Health and Education Act (DSHEA) enacted by Congress in 1994. This legislation essentially removed governmental control over supplement manufacturing and sales. The sole remaining control by the FDA occurs after the fact, when a supplement has been demonstrated to be harmful.

Another contributor to unethical drug sales and consumption is direct-to-consumer advertising, in which prescription drugs are hawked to gullible consumers via an unfortunately successful series of marketing ploys. The justification by the pharmaceutical industry for DTC advertising is education of the public. However, marketing is not education, and the public suffers from excessive drug consumption.

Unless the worst features of the DSHEA legislation are removed and effective limits placed on DTC advertising, the supplement and drug contributions to healthcare cost inflation will continue. The public is not being served properly

References

1. F. A. Hoffman, "Regulation of Dietary Supplements in the U.S.: understanding the DSHEA,"*Clin Ob and Gyn.* 44, No. 4 (December 2001). 780-88.

2. U.S. Preventive Services Task Force, "Routine Vitamin Supplementation to Prevent Cancer and Cardiovascular Disease," *Ann Int Med* 139, No. 1 (July 1, 2003): 51-55.

3. Amer Council on Science and Health, "A Cure for Heart Disease? Not Antioxidants, It Seems," (June 9, 2003).

4. S. E. Strauss, "Herbal Medicines – What's in the Bottle?," *New Eng J Med* 347, No 25, (December 18, 2005): 1997-8.

5. C. D. DeAngelis, and P. B. Fontanarosa, "Drugs Alias Dietary Supplements," JAMA 290, No 11, (September 17, 2003): 1519-20.

6. D. D. Hensrud, D. D. Engle, and M. Scheitel, "Underreporting the Use of Dietary Supplements," *Mayo Clinic Proc.* 74. (1999): 443-7.

7. J. S. Markowitz, et al, "Effect of St. John's Wort on Drug Metabolism by Induction of Enzyme," JAMA 290, No. 11 (Sept 17, 2003): 1500-9.

8. P. B. Fontanarosa, D. Rennie, and C. D. DeAngelis, "The Need for Regulation of Dietary Supplements – Lessons from Ephedra," JAMA 289, No 12. March 26, 2003): 1568-9.

9. E. Wooltarton, "Herbal Kava: Reports of Liver Toxicity," *Can Med Ass J* 166, No 6 (March 19, 2002): 777.

10. E. Ernst, "Risk-Benefit Profile of Commonly Used Herbal Therapies," *Ann Int Med* 136, No 1 (January 1, 2002): 42-52.

11. R. B. Turner, R. Bauer, et al, "An Evolution of Echinacea in Rhinovirus Infections," *N Eng J Med* 353, No 4 (2005 July 28) 337-9.

12. J. Alrich, et al, "Intra-Articular Hyaluronic Acid for Osteoarthritis of the Knee." *Can Med Ass J* 172, No 8 (2005): 1039-43.

13 B. D. Lindsay, "Are Serious Adverse Cardiovascular Events an Unintended Consequence of the DSHEA?," *Mayo Clin. Proc* 77 (January 2002): 7-9.

7

Evidence-Based Medicine

Evidence-based medicine is currently widely discussed in both medical and lay circles. Lay people commonly believe that their personal physicians utilize diagnostic and therapeutic procedures which have been studied adequately for efficacy. That is, they believe that what their doctors do has been evaluated adequately. Unfortunately, as we will point out in detail throughout this chapter, the use of evidence-based medicine is more the exception than the rule. Most medical practice derives from a hand-me-down approach, in which the medical student learns from his or her teacher and assumes that the information has been validated adequately. In fact, a great deal of medical practice has never been evaluated scientifically. Much practice derives from anecdotes, testimonials and a physician's personal experiences. Unfortunately, "experience" too often involves the repetition of error. Another contribution to the lack of evidence is the notion that a proposed medical activity "makes sense." As we have already mentioned *ad nauseam*, what "makes sense" is often not confirmed by appropriate studies.

Why is it important to utilize evidence-based medicine in the practice of medicine? Does practicing it make a difference? The practice of medicine is a combination of art and science. Without science, we reduce traditional medical practice to the level of alternative care, most of which is solely art (and fraud). So much of alternative care is based on anti-science, and its practitioners offer no scientific justification, actually ridiculing the value of providing "evidence" as traditional medicine's "hang-up." Although many of the proponents of alternative and complementary care (CAM) are well-intentioned, the majority are quacks and charlatans, who con the public for profit. As I will demonstrate, traditional medical care, when it also lacks "evidence," performs no better. Unless the practice of medicine adopts evidence-based medicine far more than it currently does, the differences between alternative care and traditional medical care may be subtle at best.

Is evidence-based medicine always a requirement of practice? Not necessarily. As much as 80 percent of perceived illnesses are self-limited, and are not influenced in intensity or duration by medical care. If diseases go away by themselves, why is it so important for physicians to use "evidence" in evaluating them? In part, the physician requires evidence to recognize that the patient's presenting problem is indeed self-limited, and thus to avoid additional diagnostic and therapeutic activities. When the disease is self-limited, the patient will save a great deal of money and effort if he or she is told that he or she will get better with time and requires no additional diagnosis or therapy. Evidence thereby contributes to cost control. If the self-limited disease is not recognized as such, excessive diagnostic and therapeutic efforts could be expended, creating additional expenses. A further negative factor is the possibility of adverse side effects of diagnosis and therapy, which always pose potential risks.

For the small proportion of human diseases worthy of medical care, possibly 10 to 20 percent, evidence is required to select the appropriate tests and therapies. This approach both saves money and is intellectually satisfying to the physician. Patients do better if the tests and therapies selected have been evaluated by evidence, rather than by a series of unscientific anecdotes, testimonials, and experiences.

Why isn't evidence-based medicine utilized more in medical practice? First, the appropriate studies to prove or disprove a proposed diagnostic or therapeutic activity are expensive and hard work. The average practitioner cannot be expected to have the time, energy, and resources necessary to perform scientific validating research. The performance of appropriate evaluating studies must be left to academic centers, government health entities, and, hopefully to a lesser extent, entrepreneurial companies. Second, researchers prefer positive results from their research efforts. Negative results are unpopular and studies have demonstrated that they are reported less.[1] It should be obvious that negative research findings are just as important as positive findings. If negative results are not reported, practicing physicians may not learn that a particular activity lacks value. In addition, if negative results remain unpublished, or hidden, other investigators might duplicate the same effort fruitlessly, presumably with similar negative findings. Another reason for the lack of reporting of negative work is financial. Drug companies do not like negative results from tests involving their pharmaceuticals and may reduce further funding for the researcher. Government is also less likely to provide grant money for researchers whose work is replete with negative results.

The final reason for the relative paucity of evidence-based medicine is the American personality. American medicine is afflicted with the same attributes as is the lay public: bigger, better, and faster. "Action" is the byword; inaction is less acceptable. All physicians have received this feedback from their patients: "He only examined and talked to me. He didn't *do* anything." It should be apparent to the reader that "doing something" is not necessarily the best way to go. A very important person said, "Don't just do something. Stand there." The result of this action orientation is the implementation of unproven technology into everyday practice long before appropriate evaluation has been performed. As I have pointed out in great detail, medical practice historically is replete with hundreds of useless diagnostic and therapeutic activities, from which thousands of patients realized no benefit, solely because appropriate evaluation had not been completed.

The premature introduction of unproven medical procedures creates multiple medical problems.[2] The most obvious is inflation of costs. Modern technology involves the use of very expensive procedures. The un-indicated and inadequately evaluated tests or therapies become a waste of healthcare dollars. Tests or therapies performed without evidence of their value often have adverse side effects. Any test or therapy has a finite incidence of adverse effects, some particularly serious. Inadequately evaluated activities divert the clinician from the correct path of patient management, delaying or confusing the diagnosis. In other words, evidence-based medicine is both cost saving and leads to better patient care. I will now provide several examples showing that the lack of evidence-based medicine has cost society a lot of money and offered little or no benefit to the patient.

LACK OF EVIDENCE-BASED MEDICINE

Internal Mammary Artery Ligation

My favorite example of the absence of evidence-based medicine is an historical one, dating back to the '50s or '60s. At the time, angina pectoris (i.e., pain in the chest) was common and disabling to many patients because modern therapies were then unavailable. Angina was due to narrowing of the coronary arteries by atherosclerosis or hardening of the arteries. When the patient exerted him or herself, requiring the heart to pump more blood through the body in order to satisfy the increased need, the patient's narrowed coronaries prevented adequate flow. This inadequacy manifested as crushing chest discomfort requiring the person to rest or reduce activity. Keep in mind that therapy at that time was quite limited. The sole medication of value was sublingual (i.e., taken beneath the tongue) nitroglycerin or other nitrate compounds. The various cardiac interventional techniques, such as coronary bypass and angioplasty, were unavailable. Because the condition was common and therapy of little value, patients were ready to try anything. That stimulus led to internal mammary artery ligation. A few surgeons theorized that these small and apparently unnecessary arteries could be readily ligated (i.e., tied off), which would divert arterial blood flow to the nearby coronaries, thereby increasing coronary perfusion (i.e., flow of blood in the arteries). A few surgeons tried the technique because it "made sense." Early results were impressive. As many as 90 – 95 percent of the patients reported significant improvement in their angina. Surgeons loved the operation. It was simple to perform and patients recovered from the surgery promptly. To everyone involved, it was "the best of all possible worlds" (as Pangloss says in Voltaire's *Candide*). Thousands of internal mammary artery ligations were performed. It was truly a surgical growth industry.

Then Dr. C. Walton Lillehei of the University of Minnesota became involved. Dr. Lillehei, very much involved in the beginnings of open-heart surgery, was already highly regarded as a great surgeon. He had an extensive private referral practice from the Upper Midwest. Many patients were therefore referred to him for internal mammary artery ligation. Lillehei was less impressed with the theory of the procedure than the other surgeons and asked himself (and others) some incisive questions. How do we know that coronary blood flow is indeed enhanced by the procedure? Unfortunately, the question was easier to ask than answer. Measuring the arterial blood flow in human patients was not yet generally possible. More importantly, Lillehei raised possibility of a placebo effect (i.e., sham or fake) accounting for the "outstanding" clinical results of the therapy. After all, angina pectoris is strictly a subjective patient complaint, lacking in any objective measurement. These people wanted to feel better and the surgeons wanted good results. The whole scene was conducive to placebo effect. Lillehei decided to test this possibility with an evidence-based experiment.

Because he had a large referral practice of patients sent to him for the ligation, he had access to an adequate patient population for his experiment. He randomly assigned patients to two groups, one group receiving the real operation and a second group having only a sham surgical procedure. Keep in mind that fifty years ago patient disclosure rules did not exist. Actually, neither the patients nor the referring physicians were told that Lillehei was doing the experiment. Since the operation was simple, the patients never knew whether they had the real procedure or the sham. Both groups had identical short surgical procedures; operating and anesthesia time were carefully maintained equally for both groups. The surgeon (Lillehei) had no control over which procedure was done. He was given a card at the start of the operation instructing him to perform either the real procedure or the sham operation.

After the surgery, the patients were instructed to return for evaluation one month later, at no additional cost, to be examined by an independent cardiologist. The latter did not know to which group any particular patient belonged. This is now called a double-blind experiment, in which both the patient and the evaluating physician don't know whether the patient was in the test case group or the control group. After a statistically significant number of cases were done, the performance data of each group was calculated. To everyone's surprise (though not to Lillehei's), 95 percent of each group had "good" or "excellent" results. The entire value of the procedure related to placebo effect. The University of Washington performed a similar experiment.[3]

Fortunately, Lillehei was sufficiently famous for this experiment to achieve widespread publicity. The procedure was then abandoned, but not until tens of thousands of patients received internal mammary ligations. Had Lillehei not been inquisitive, the procedure might have been inflicted upon thousands of other patients. We are now more aware of the role of the placebo effect in any form of therapy, and appropriate controls are experimentally available to minimize the effect.

Gastric Freezing

The gastric freezing work of Dr. Owen Wangensteen, also of the University of Minnesota in the late '60s, provides another example of implementing a procedure that "makes sense" without prior evaluation. It had already been demonstrated that cooling the stomach was effective in reducing gastric hemorrhage in patients with bleeding peptic ulcers. The lowered temperature reduces acid production by the lining mucosa, enabling the ulcer to heal and to cease the bleeding. Wangensteen used iced saline solution to cool the stomach. Some enterprising entrepreneurs, with some medical assistance, reasoned that cooling the stomach would also be useful in treating peptic ulcers in general. They developed a cooling machine in which refrigerated solution was circulated through coils placed in the stomach. Since this was an era of high incidence of ulcer disease and relatively ineffective therapy, the machines were sold and used widely. Before long, disasters occurred. The machines worked too well, freezing the abdominal wall and rupturing the frozen stomach. Many deaths resulted and the equipment was abandoned. I can only wonder how many plaintiff attorneys became involved in these therapeutic misadventures.

Bone Marrow Transplant to Augment High Dose Chemotherapy (BMT/HDC)

A more recent example of inadequate prior evaluation involves the practice of bone marrow transplant to augment high dose chemotherapy (BMT/HDC) for women with advanced breast cancer. [4] These unfortunate women were typically young, with growing families. This procedure was introduced to treat women with aggressive breast cancers in whom recurrence was already documented. These patients had been treated with standard chemotherapy, with some therapeutic response. The theory was that, because conventional chemotherapy yielded some positive therapeutic response, a much larger dose of the same drugs might achieve an even better response, perhaps even a cure. However, a "much larger" dose would cause fatal consequences, particularly to body systems sensitive to chemotherapy. The bone marrow, the source of rapidly multiplying blood cells, is very sensitive to chemotherapy and radiation.

BMT/HDC involves harvesting the patient's bone marrow in advance, treating the patients with huge doses of chemotherapy and/or radiation, and then reinfusing the stored bone marrow. Despite major expense and significant mortality from the procedure, initial results suggested extended survival and even apparent "cures."

The introduction of BMT/HDC engendered a tremendous social pressure to expand the use of the therapy. Because the outcome of the recurrent cancer was considered to be absolutely grim, many found the expense and the risk entailed by having the procedure acceptable. The choice appeared to be life or death; almost all of the available recipients of BMT/HDC opted for the therapy. As is true of so many newly introduced diagnostic or therapeutic procedures, the therapy "made sense" and initial impressions of its value supported that view. Unfortunately, the therapy was introduced with far more hoopla and unrealistic expectations than evidence. Some of the centers performing the combined therapy were quick to point out that they were on the "cutting edge" of care and that those not involved were falling behind. However, the oncologists at my institution did not jump on the therapeutic bandwagon, bur rather insisted on evidence of true success. Unfortunately, evidence was hard to come by because of the attendant hoopla.

The health insurance industry, rather than involved physicians, may have played a vital role in the performance of a much needed clinical study. The industry initially refused to cover the procedure on the basis that it was "experimental." As chance would have it, a Minnesota legislator's wife was a candidate for the BMT/HDC procedure and he introduced legislation mandating insurance coverage successfully. (One might suggest that the legislature was into the practice of medicine.) Eventually, a national study was funded, statistically requiring eight hundred participants, half receiving BMT/HDC and the other half receiving standard chemotherapy for advanced, recurrent breast cancer.[5] The study could not be double-blind; the patients would obviously "know" which half of the study they were in. Only the objective measures of mortality and disease-free interval would be determined. The latter simply was the time beyond therapy after which the disease became obvious again.

The big problem was enlisting eight hundred participants. Almost none of the potential participants wanted to be in the control group, making enlistment very difficult. To avoid selection bias, the women who participated had to agree in advance that they would be part of a control group 50 percent of the time. To encourage enlistment, some centers refused to perform the procedure on any patient who would not participate in the study. The Mayo Clinic in particular accepted patients into the study only if they agreed in advance to be part of the control group if necessary.

Finally, the required eight hundred participants were enlisted and the study performed, with two years elapsing for evaluation of the results. The results revealed *no* difference between the BMT/HDC group and the control group in terms of mortality and disease-free interval. The sole difference was expense and initial mortality of the combined therapy. To my knowledge, the study ended the therapy, but not until thousands of cases had been done. Once again, we can see the importance of having evidence of success prior to adopting any new procedure.

Knee Arthroscopy

Another recent example of a new procedure being used without prior evaluation is the practice of arthroscopic surgery on the knee in patients with osteoarthritis (i.e., chronic deterioration of the knee cartilage). These patients suffer from chronic pain on weight-bearing joints and have significant limitation of function. Arthroscopic surgery seemed to be a modest therapeutic effort far easier on the patient than an open knee operation and it promised impressive results. The procedure involved either gavage (i.e., the washing out of joint space debris) or debridement (i.e., the smoothing out of rough or torn cartilage surfaces). The theory behind the procedure was that debris in the joint space or rough joint cartilage surfaces perpetuated the inflammatory process. If the debris was removed and the cartilage surface improved, the swelling would be minimized. The goal was to reduce the symptoms so that a much larger procedure (specifically, total joint replacement) could be delayed or avoided. The theory made eminently "good sense," and because many people suffered from these joint problems, many arthroscopic procedures were performed. One estimate is that 650,000 arthroscopies were performed in 1988, at a cost of five thousand dollars for each case. This surgery became part of a truly impressive growth industry. Results initially were good, proving to the involved orthopedists that the theory "made sense." Arthroscopic gavage and debridement of knee osteoarthritis became the "standard of care."

Finally some inquisitive orthopedic academicians asked the appropriate questions. They reasoned that the theory behind the procedure made little sense and that the activity had no enduring value. The basic pathology of the disorder, erosion or destruction of joint cartilage, was not corrected by the process. Accordingly, a multi-center controlled trial of the procedure was performed, involving a double-blind study.[6] Although the involved patients realized that they were part of a study, the trial was conducted in such a fashion that the patients did not know

whether they were in the test group or in the half with a sham procedure. Further, the evaluation was performed by a separate group of
orthopedists who also did not know to which group the patients they
were studying belonged. At the conclusion of the study, the results indicated that both groups had identical pain relief and function. Much of
the enthusiasm for the procedure was thus due to the placebo effect.
The theoretical basis for the arthroscopy, although it "made sense," did
not stand after a statistically valid clinical trial. One can only speculate
if the negative results of this study have led to an increase in much larger procedures such as total knee replacements. At least the large operation addresses the basic pathology of the disorder.

Imaging of the Spine

Moving away from therapeutic procedures, we will discuss some
advanced imaging tests designed to improve the diagnosis of chronic
back pain disorders. The basic problem with chronic back pain syn-
dromes is that a specific diagnosis is usually unobtainable. This common
condition is often attacked surgically, all too often without a positive
result. In fact, many conservative surgeons believe that a surgical
approach to chronic back problems may only serve to worsen a chronic
problem. To improve back pain diagnoses, CT scans or MRIs, procedures that have become integral parts of the imaging expansion contributing so much to healthcare cost inflation, were introduced. These
advanced imaging procedures were clearly superior to plain x-rays of the
spine given their ability to reveal more clearly abnormalities of the
spine. The abnormalities thus demonstrated became the reason for more
back surgeries. But are patients better served with more back surgery?
The evidence is hard to come by. Some have suggested that the improved
resolution offered by advanced imaging rarely predicts an improved
clinical outcome for the patient.

Finally some academic radiologists performed a study examining the
relationship of imaging findings to patient symptoms.[7] They examined a
large group of patients with MRI studies, including persons with back
symptoms as well as persons without backaches. They found that many

individuals had abnormal anatomy but did not have backaches. The study demonstrated that symptoms associated with abnormalities seen on MRI studies were purely coincidental. The documented imaging abnormalities provided no indication for surgical intervention. Further, if patients without pain learn that they have abnormal discs they might adopt illness-related behavior such as skipping work. The sole justification for advanced imaging procedures should be preparation for patients scheduled for surgery on clinical grounds, other than the presence of abnormalities depicted on the MRI.

The expansion of imaging activities in the evaluation of patients with back pain is again a predominantly American phenomenon. A likely result of this expansion is a corresponding increase in back surgery. The United States and the United Kindom show the most dramatic difference in back surgery rates with the United States rate five times that of England and Scotland. Part of the reason for the difference in surgery rate is the presence of more neurologic and orthopedic surgeons in the American population. When there are more surgeons capable of performing back surgery, more back surgery will be the result. But should the availability of surgeons be the justification for performing an elective operation? More importantly, do Americans benefit from this obvious surfeit of back surgery?[8] Probably not. At least there are no randomized trials evaluating the effectiveness of spine surgery for chronic backache. In fact, the opposite is probably true. In so many cases, patients with chronic backaches subjected to surgery are either no better or are worsened.

Swan-Ganz Catheter

A particularly nefarious medical procedure has been the use of pulmonary-artery (better known as Swan-Ganz) catheters for high-risk surgical patients requiring intensive care. A large Canadian study demonstrated convincingly that mortality was not affected by the use of S-G catheters.[9] Up until recently, upwards of one million S-G catheters were placed each year with costs of over two billion dollars. How can the practice be continued despite numerous studies demonstrating its

lack of value? As is true of so many "procedures," the use of S-G catheter "made sense." Although many arguments are used to justify their
use, perhaps the most insidious one is that it is "unethical to withhold"
their use. One might suggest that the proven lack of value makes it
"unethical to utilize."

Perhaps a personal anecdote might reveal still another illogical justification. In one of my personal visits to the Royal London Hospital as
a visiting educator, I attended a Grand Rounds presentation of an unusually complex case. The young patient was involved in a serious automobile accident, and suffered multiple fractures, a lacerated liver, a
perforated bowel (of both the large and small intestines), and a transient
head injury. Complications during the three-week hospitalization
included peritonitis, gram negative septicemia, acute lung injury, and
profound shock with renal shutdown. Doctors were amazed he survived.
As I heard the case, it occurred to me that something was missing; no
Swan-Ganz catheter had been used. The case was managed entirely with
a few simple radiological studies, the measurement of fluid balance, some
selected acid-base and electrolyte studies, and, of course, much clinical
consideration and judgment. No CT scans or MRI studies were done. At
the conclusion of the Rounds, I asked the discusser why an S-G catheter
was not used to assist in the management of this extremely complex
management. That certainly would have been the case in the "colonies."
He scratched his chin and said dryly, "If I were paid three hundred dollars to insert an S-G catheter, I would certainly have done so."

Hormone Replacement Therapy

My final example of the damage done by the absence of evidence-
based medicine receives abundant public exposure and a great deal of
emotional response. That subject is hormonal replacement therapy
(HRT) for menopausal symptoms. The debate about the value of estrogen replacement dates back at least a half century. I can recall discus-
sions in my medical student years. Some academic gynecologists took
the position that, if the designer (possibly God) of the human body
wanted women to reproduce later in life, he (or she?) would not have
designed the ovary to fail during menopause. One could argue that the

design reflects the reproductive limits of women. Perhaps women should not bear children past a certain age.

There is no doubt that the decline in estrogen production by the ovary leads to the common menopausal symptoms; vasomotor instability (i.e., hot flashes and excessive perspiration) and vaginal mucosal dryness. Estrogen therapy became an effective treatment of these symptoms quickly. At one time, as many as 40 percent of American women took HRT using, for example, Premarin, an equine conjugated estrogen. Although the major vendor of estrogens would have preferred that all women take estrogen during their menopause when they introduced their products, a majority did not. A small minority of women never had hot flashes. A significant number accepted menopausal symptoms as the facts of life. They endured the symptoms, which eventually relent.

It was quickly determined that estrogen replacement alone stimulated the endometrium (the uterine lining) and predisposed to endometrial cancer, a relatively indolent cancer. It was believed that by combining estrogen with a progestin, thereby mimicking the hormonal production of the menstrual cycle, the unopposed estrogen stimulus would be minimized and the risk of an endometrial cancer reduced. Therefore, for women with a uterus, combined HRT was recommended and widely used.

For reasons unclear to me, the value of HRT in reducing vasomotor instability and vaginal dryness was expanded. Some of this was undoubtedly due to the marketing efforts of estrogen manufacturers. HRT may have been recommended by physicians who curried favor with their menopausal patients. Still others honestly believed that some negative symptoms of menopause could be delayed by replacing estrogen. It was now claimed that HRT could help put off coronary heart disease, reduce osteoporosis (i.e., bone softening), better "nerves" and sleep habits, prevent Alzheimer's disease, reduce skin wrinkles, and retain the "bloom of life." Women generally accepted these potential benefits as fact, and there can be little doubt that the estrogen manufacturers contributed to the myths of these unproven indications. For example, the manufacturer of Premarin (Ayerst) hired Lauren Hutton, super-model, to suggest that her beauty was due to using Premarin. Isn't that convincing?

The belief that HRT would reduce or delay the progress of coronary heart disease in women had an interesting pathophysiologic basis. It was widely recognized that men were afflicted with coronary disease ten to fifteen years earlier than were women. The belief was that the ovaries' estrogen production protected women's coronary arteries, at least until menopause. Indeed, coronary heart disease was relatively rare in women until they reached menopause, with the rare exception of women with inherited cholesterol conditions. Whereas men would have heart attacks in their thirties or forties, women would rarely have such cardiac events until after the menopause. It "made sense" that ovarian estrogen production was protective and that HRT would continue the protection into later years. However, as has been pointed out repeatedly, what "makes sense" must withstand the scrutiny of controlled studies. Those studies materialized when the Women's Health Initiative (WHI), reported the results of a monumental study.[10]

The WHI study was a large, double-blind study comparing women taking a combined estrogen-progestin preparation with a comparable group of women taking only a placebo. To the consternation of those who supported HRT during menopause, the study indicated both increased risks and the absence of advertised benefits of HRT. In fact the study found that coronary events were increased, particularly in the early years of therapy, despite the presumption that estrogen would delay coronary disease. Further, the study reported a significant increase in breast cancer incidence, resulting in premature discontinuance of this study. Although there was evidence that HRT somewhat reduced osteoporosis, this advantage was considered of less importance than the problematic increase in breast cancer. As a direct result of this discontinued study, HRT use was discouraged, except in cases of women with overwhelming menopausal symptomatology, and even then, HRT was only used for as short a period as possible.

Contrasting the conclusion of the WHI, the Nurses' Health Study (NHS) came up with different results.[11] The NHS concluded that coronary disease *was* reduced by HRT. The disparate findings may be due to differences in the designs of the two studies. The NHS was "observational," a reporting by nurses of their HRT use and their incidence of heart disease. This approach, in which appropriate randomization of test and control groups does not occur, engenders the statistical bias of "selection." The WHI, on the other hand, was a valid, double-blind study.

Not only was HRT not found useful in delaying coronary disease, but it seemed to increase incidences of strokes and other coagulation disorders. The degree to which HRT helped sustain the "bloom of life" and "better nerves and sleep" was not evaluated. These parameters are too vague for objective evaluation. We should be embarrassed to have permitted the lapsing of so many years before we found out the truth of the value of HRT. Why did it take so long? After all, millions of American women took estrogens for the menopausal symptoms under false pretenses, accepting the promotion of profit-oriented marketers and the effusive blandishments of proponents who likely had ulterior motives. We must resist endorsing what "makes sense" and subject therapies to the unbiased scrutiny of controlled clinical trials (CRTs). We owe this to our patients. Furthermore, we can help control healthcare cost inflation if we use evidence-based medicine.

EVIDENCE-BASED KNOWLEDGE WITHOUT IMPLEMENTATION

We will now venture beyond discussing the lack of evaluation and address evaluative studies that medical practice doesn't yet consider. The following examples are not of rare or exotic disease disorders seldom seen in everyday medical practice. The examples represent ordinary clinical disorders that primary care physicians and assorted specialists see regularly, but whose "evidence" the physicians either ignore or compromise.

Acute URI

Acute upper respiratory infections, including the common cold, represent frequent conditions that if untreated, run a predictable and finite clinical course. These conditions for the most part do not require medical care. Fortunately, most cases are not seen by physicians and the person who does not seek help does equally as well or better than those who seek medical attention. As we pointed out earlier, when patients with self-limited diseases are seen in a healthcare setting, they usually only receive a bill and perhaps make their conditions worse. The person who uses Kleenex, nose drops, and proprietary cough medicine for the common cold does as well as the patient who is prescribed expensive broad-spectrum antibiotics for a viral infection. The vast majority of URIs are caused by viruses which do not respond to antibiotic therapy and for which antibiotics should *not* be administered. Any yet, if the patient with an acute URI seeks medical aid, he or she might very well receive an antibiotic. If lucky, the person will only lose his or her money. If less fortunate, the person may get an enduring bout of diarrhea caused by changes in intestinal bacterial flora.

In a great many cases, the patient seeks medical attention after days with the URI. The patient is convinced that the physician will prescribe a medication that will reduce the duration and intensity of the illness. It may well be that the disorder has already peaked at about the time of the visit, and that the patient would improve in a short time with or without medical care. The only people with prolonged or more severe symptoms are those with known respiratory tract allergies or who smoke cigarettes. These people have longer and more intense symptoms.

Most patients with URIs have some degree of cough.[12] They may cough up sputum, some of which may be colored green. The pharmaceutical companies that market antibiotics have been quite successful in convincing physicians that cough, with or without sputum production, is "bronchitis" caused by susceptible bacteria. This is utter nonsense. A common feature of most URIs is cough; bacterial "bronchitis" rarely exists. URIs with cough improve equally well with or without antibiotics. Using prescription antibiotics benefits only the drug companies. In addition to increasing costs and causing potential side effects, using antibiotics frequently leads to antibiotic resistance.

During my brief stint in primary care, I had a patient who insisted on antibiotic therapy. I was asked to evaluate a man with a "bad cold."

He informed me that the senior physicians in the practice always gave him a "shot of penicillin" to "kick the cold." I examined him, concluded that he had a common cold, and advised him to use over-the-counter symptomatic therapy. He insisted on a "shot of penicillin," and no matter how strongly I pointed out that penicillin would make no difference in the course of his cold, he remained adamant. He eventually stormed out, pointing out that he would not pay for this office call. When I later described the experience to the older physicians in the practice, they were amused. They argued that I could have charged extra for the "shot," the patient would still have gotten well, and he would have been content. The experience served to convince me that I would not be comfortable compromising my medical judgment repeatedly in a primary care career. I soon left general practice and became a pathologist.

Adult Sore Throat

Adult sore throat is a variant of a URI, in which there is no rhinitis (or runny nose) or cough. The magnificent work of three University of Minnesota pediatricians decades ago demonstrated that the appropriate treatment for conditions involving group A streptococcal pharyngitis (i.e., "strep throat") also prevented acute rheumatic fever (ARF). Indeed, ARF was a very severe heart valve inflammation resulting in major heart disease. Unfortunately, as far as ARF is concerned, this monumental advance in basic science came a little late. For reasons which are still debated and probably unclear, doctors no longer see ARF in everyday medical practice. However, the testing for "strep throat" is a billion-dollar medical industry. Taking a throat culture is the law of the land for physicians with patients with any symptom of a sore throat. If group A streptococci is identified, physicians recommend penicillin therapy to both treat the diseased throat and prevent ARF. As Pangloss would say, this was "The best of all possible worlds." But what was really accomplished?

Streptococcal pharyngitis is also a self-limited condition, responding in a few days with or without therapy. Since ARF no longer appears to be a problem, what is the advantage of treating streptococcal sore throat? This question is particularly relevant in cases of adults with sore throat. ARF was always rare in adults, and there is no evidence that antibiotic therapy shortens the duration of sore throats. An increasing level of opinion currently suggests that physicians should not treat sore throats, other than with lozenges. Unfortunately, it is very difficult to retard the steamroller of medical activity after decades of practice. I doubt very much that anything I could say to discourage taking throat cultures and prescribing antibiotic therapy will change these practices.

Acute Backache

Acute episodes of back pain occur in most people at some time in their lives. The condition comes on spontaneously without obvious cause, or may occur as the result of some back strain. In either case, it is indeed debilitating and disabling, a condition the average person may not tolerate and for which he or she might seek medical consultation.

Solid evidence is available about how to handle most cases of acute backache. The condition is self-limited; 80 percent or more spontaneously subside in two weeks. The condition has been studied adequately and appropriate therapeutic recommendations which are effective in the great majority of instances are available. No longer recommended are spine x-rays, muscle relaxants, bedrest or physical therapy. What works best is continued activity and the use of simple over-the-counter analgesics (i.e., pain pills). Unfortunately, if the hurting person seeks medical attention during the acute state, particularly if he visits an urgent care center or emergency room, physicians will likely recommend bedrest, muscle relaxants, x-rays, and possibly diathermy or therapeutic ultrasound.

Additional Technology Follies

In addition to instances when medical practice ignores evidence-based medicine, there are other religiously-held forms of medical care the practice of which defies explanation. I am amazed at the continued use of electronic fetal monitoring during labor, ostensibly designed to identify fetal distress early enough so that the medical staff can intervene therapeutically and save an infant. The practice was begun decades ago without evidence of its need, and this intensive technology was widely adopted, its use becoming the "standard of care" in most American hospitals. When the required randomized control trials were finally done, the consensus of several good studies demonstrated that the practice conferred no benefit to the fetus and yet posed an increased risk of operative delivery (i.e., cesarean section or forceps delivery).[13] Intermittent auscultation (or stethoscope listening) by obstetric nurses accomplishes what electronic monitoring accomplishes. With all this evidence, how can we justify continuing the practice? The nurses seem to love it; patients are duly impressed with the gadgetry; equipment manufacturers reap benefits; and hospitals can make an additional charge. The practice is ridiculous, if not obscene. One also wonders if plaintiff attorneys encourage the use of an outdated form of diagnosis. If monitoring is the "standard of care" and an infant does not do well, parents might sue.

Another even more recent and nefarious obstetric practice is home uterine activity monitoring during pregnancy.[14] The goal is to detect premature labor as early as possible, thereby enabling effective therapy to reduce the complications of delivering prematurely. The practice "makes sense," doesn't it? Control studies revealed that expensive monitoring with telemetry was no more effective in preventing preterm births than was ordinary care. Of interest is the fact that some obstetricians who utilized this useless activity had a financial interest in the manufacture and utilization of the equipment. Not only is evidence ignored in this case, but a nefarious profit motive appears to be involved.

The final obstetrics example involves the almost universal practice of episiotomy (i.e., the surgical enlargement of the birth canal) during the second stage of labor, particularly in primipara (i.e., first term pregnancy). The almost universally accepted reason for doing an episiotomy is to improve the second stage of labor, shortening the time and sparing the infant additional trauma. The second stated purpose is to prevent undesirable obstetric complications, notably third degree perineal tears.

A recent study examined multiple prior studies of the value of episiotomy and determined that it failed to improve the obstetric practice, aid the fetus, or minimize complications.[15] Despite the fact that millions of episiotomies have been performed, ostensibly for reasons which "make sense," only recently has an objective evaluation of their value been performed. Does this new information mean that the practice will be eliminated? Given my experience with the stubbornness rampant in obstetricians and knowing their dedication to unproven procedures, I maintain that nothing will change.

I could describe hundreds of additional procedures that either have never been evaluated for efficacy or about which solid evidence is ignored. The above examples should provide adequate support for the importance of evidence-based medicine and its appropriate utilization.

FACTORS HINDERING EVIDENCE-BASED MEDICINE

One might wonder why the unhappy situation I've described exists. One might believe that evidence-based practice should be standard. Why, indeed, aren't appropriate studies performed and solid information used?

A variety of socio-economic factors may be involved. Some of the factors are not unique to medical practice. Social changes in medical practice have converted a once noble profession into just another way to earn a living. In an earlier time, medical practice was an all-consuming calling, in which physicians placed the welfare of their patients far above their personal needs. Although this professional emphasis may have been costly to the physician's personal and family life, it was advantageous to the patient. Physicians venturing into practice upon completion of their professional education now are often more interested in call schedules, benefits, vacations, and wages than they are in the professional aspects of a practice. The "bottom line" attributes of most managed care businesses infect physician practice, particularly as it affects physicians' living standards.

Other economic handicaps to better medical practice involve the growth of urgent care centers and the utilization of the emergency room as a primary care facility. These changes are an expected byproduct of the need for economic efficiencies in physicians' offices. Regularly scheduled appointments are efficient; fitting in acutely ill patients creates problems. Urgent care and ER visits proliferate because patients are unable to see their regular doctors when acutely ill. Seeing a strange physician in an acute situation obviates the value of continuity of care. The environment created lends itself to procedure-oriented care, with more therapy than is needed. Only rarely does a child with a URI who is seen in an urgent care center not get an antibiotic prescription.

Another impediment to evidence-based medicine and cost-effective care is the trend in physicians to prescribe technical procedures at the expense of doing cognitive clinical evaluation. If physicians used less sophisticated technology and did more thoughtful consideration, costs would fall dramatically and quality of care would likely increase. Physicians made effective diagnoses before CT scans, MRIs, and interventional radiology were available. These procedures, of course, have their place and use. Unfortunately, their ready availability makes it easy to overutilize them at the expense of thinking through the problem. The great stimulus to using procedures, beyond their availability, is remunerative. Complex procedures provide far better compensation than do other medical efforts. An interventional radiologist can be paid more for one complicated procedure than for reading dozens of plain x-ray films. A gastroenterologist is paid more for one endoscopic procedure than for seeing ten patients in the office.

Entrepreneurial factors, almost always including a desire for financial gain, affect medical practice. Free-standing surgical centers have proliferated, and surgeons benefit in two ways. In addition to charging for their surgical skill, they are also rewarded when people use the facility if they have a financial interest in the surgery center. Further, since such facilities are expensive to operate, it behooves the surgeon to keep it occupied and thus to encourage patients to have surgery. The economic concerns of a free-standing facility certainly do not relate to concerns for evidence-based care.

Entrepreneurial zeal is also evident in the proliferation of free-standing imaging centers. Income-oriented radiologists permit plaintiff attorneys and chiropractors to refer well-heeled lay people to come in and order their own studies, all without physician referral. They also encourage walk-ins. These centers offer all the most recently-described procedures, with little apparent concern for either a patient's need for the tests or the efficacy of the tests. The sole consideration is profit. The spiral helical CT scan is a classic example of an unproven imaging "procedure" being quickly put into practice without study. Cigarette smokers request the new test ostensibly to detect a lung cancer earlier than is possible with other existing technology. It not only has not been demonstrated to reduce lung cancer mortality, but it provides the smoker with a false sense of security. Smokers would be far better served if they quit smoking rather than spend foolish dollars on unproven and ineffective imaging tests.

Entrepreneurial incursions into the profession of medical practice may simply be a symptom of everything else happening in the United States. Economic factors have achieved preeminence in medical decision-making. Simply doing the best possible work was once a pleasure in itself. Nowadays superior accomplishments, rather than being goals by themselves, are graded by the profits they generate.

SUMMARY

Although there is widespread belief that traditional medical practice is evidence-based, most medical practice has never been evaluated scientifically. Everyday practice is essentially the result of a hand-me-down approach, in which practice derives from anecdotes, testimonials, and experience. Contributing to the lack of evidence is the idea that a proposed diagnostic or therapeutic endeavor "makes sense" and that, therefore, statistically valid verification is unnecessary.

Without evidence, traditional medicine is reduced to the level of most complementary and alternative medicine (CAM), in which scientific rigor is non-existent. Not only has much medical practice not been subjected to evidence-based evaluation, it also ignores evidence when such evidence is available.

A typical scenario entails introducing a new diagnostic or a therapeutic activity because it "makes sense" and implementing it before any semblance of validation has occurred. After thousands of these "procedures" have been done, some curious investigator performs the necessary evaluation and discovers that the activity has little or no value. Not only is this proliferation of useless activities of no value to patient care, but it significantly contributes to our current healthcare cost inflation.

In recent times, national organizations have conducted evaluations of everyday practice activities and reported that the practices have no value. The prime example is the demonstration that hormone replacement therapy (HRT) for menopause not only did not accomplish what was claimed, but increased the incidence of some medical problems.

A typical example of ignoring evidence-based medicine involves the use of antibiotics in treating viral respiratory infections. Not only does this practice create adverse side effects and contribute to antibiotic resistance, but it is a major drug cost factor in health inflation.

Until medicine assumes a scientific basis, utilizing evidence-based information, patient care will be compromised and healthcare cost inflation will continue.

The goal of achieving almost universal evidence-based medicine may be utopian. Too many factors, many of which prevent the search for the truth in medical activity, compete for the attention of medical practitioners. The scientific basis of the practice of medicine demands that we exert more efforts in the search for the real value of our efforts. Evidence-based medicine is not simply a utopian, theoretical goal. Practicing it is the best way to give our patients the best care achievable. We can improve care and realize the long-term goal of reducing healthcare cost inflation at the same time.

References

1. D. M. Ilstrup, "Randomized Clinical Trials: Potential Cost Savings Due to Identification of Ineffective Medical Therapies," *Mayo Clin Proc* 70 (1995): 707-10.

2. D. A. Grimes, "Technology Follies: The Uncritical Acceptance of Medical Innovation," *JAMA* 269, No 23 (June 16, 1993): 3030-32.

3. L. Cobb, C. Thomas, et al, "An Evolutionary Internal Mammary Ligation." *N Eng J Med* 260 (1950): 1115.

4. M. M. Mello and T. A. Brennan, "The Cancer Controversy Over High-Dose Chemotherapy with Autologous Bone Marrow Transplant for Breast Cancer," *Health Affairs* (September/October 2001): 101-17.

5. E. A. Stadtmauer, et al, "Conventional Chemotherapy Compared with High-Dose Chemotherapy Plus Bone Marrow Transplant for Metastatic Breast Cancer," *N Eng J Med* 342, No 15 (2000): 1069-76.

6. Mosely J. B. Mosely, et al, "A Controlled Trial of Arthroscopic Surgery for Osteoarthritis of the Knee," *N Eng J Med* 347, No 2 (July 11, 2002): 81 - 88.

7. M. C. Jensen, et al, "Magnetic Resonance Imaging of the Spine in People Without Back Pain," *N Eng J Med* 331, No. 2 (July 14, 1994): 69-73.

8. S. J. Atlas, R. B. Keller, Y. A. Wu, et al, "Long-Term Outcomes of Surgical and Non-Surgical Management of Sciatica Secondary to Lumbar Disc Herniation," *Spine* 30 (2005): 29.

9. J. D. Sandham, et al, "A Randomized, Controlled Trial of the Use of Pulmonary-Artery Catheters in High-Risk Surgical Patients," *N Eng J Med* 348 (2003): 5.

10. S. W. Fletcher and G. A. Calditz, "Failure of Estrogen Therapy for Prevention," *JAMA* 288, No 3 (July 17, 2002): 366-7.

11. F. Grodstein et al, "Postmenopausal Use and Prevention of Coronary Events in the Nurses' Health Study," *Ann Int Med* 3 135, No 1 (July 2006): 1-8.

12. M. H. Ebell, "Antibiotic Prescribing for Cough and Symptoms of Respiratory Tract Infection," *JAMA* 293 No 24 (June 22/29, 2005): 3062-4.

13. Grimes, *Technology Follies*: 3030-32.

14. Grimes, *Technology Follies*: 3030-32.

15. K. Hartmann, et al, "Outcomes of Episiotomy," *JAMA* 293, No. 17 (May 4, 2005): 2141-8.

8

Real Preventive Medicine

The lay concept that an annual health evaluation will prolong one's life and improve the quality of health has had widespread acceptance for at least a century. Having an annual physical examination was promoted by the American Medical Association in 1920. At the time, this was a surprising recommendation, since medical care didn't have the resources to treat most of the detected abnormalities. The recommendation presumably "made sense," and so was not refuted.

The theoretical rationale for having an annual health evaluation is to detect diseases earlier, when therapy supposedly is more effective. The assumption is that diseases are often asymptomatic but can still be diagnosed. If diagnosed early, before the diseases cause symptoms, therapy should be more effective. Although this rationale may be true in isolated instances, evidence to support the thesis is hard to come by. Proponents of the annual physical cite examples in which early detection of a disease led to successful therapy. The proponents give credit to early detection for the successful management. These anecdotes don't address the possibility that the "successful" therapy might just as likely have occurred at a later stage of the disease, when symptoms were present. As we pointed out in our discussion of "evidence-based medicine," these anecdotes of "success" often lack a control group against which we can compare success and failure.

Most surveys of public expectations and attitudes discerning the value of having an annual physical indicate that the public supports the concept unequivocally. [1] And why shouldn't they? Most major medical organizations have endorsed the annual physical for decades, particularly since the end of World War II. An additional source of support is the emergence of health maintenance organizations (HMOs), whose very name implies the positive value of a periodic health examination.

More recently, research has yielded hard evidence about the true yield of the value of the annual exam. Major health organizations agree that the annual physical, as it is done, has scant yield and should be abandoned in favor of a more selective evaluation. In particular, the American College of Physicians (an organization of physicians in internal medicine), the AMA, and the US Preventive Services Task Force (USPSTF) have de-emphasized the value of the routine annual physical.[2] Further, surveys suggest that the public attitude towards annual physicals varies according to what is involved in the exam, and whether or not the cost of the service is out-of-pocket. Whereas almost all agree to the value of blood pressure measurement, few support hearing and vision measurement. Relatively few support blood glucose measurement and chest x-rays. The numbers of people supporting even some annual tests dramatically decrease if the costs are assessed to the patient directly.

Although one should avoid anecdotes to prove a point, permit me to utilize one for effect. A good friend, a successful businessman, visited the Mayo Clinic for an annual physical regularly. This exam was over two days and included numerous blood tests, some imaging procedures, and endoscopy. On one visit, after many years of annual health evaluations, a mild abnormality showed up in a liver function test. Subsequent study revealed that he had inherited hemochromatosis, an iron storage disease, which included advanced hepatic cirrhosis. For reasons that remain unclear, serum iron was not part of the battery of chemistry tests performed. And so, unfortunately, the one test that would have made a difference was not included in his previous chemistry screens. The patient's history somehow didn't indicate that many of his relatives had "liver disease," diabetes, and had died prematurely. Had he had a single iron blood test during one of his many annual physicals, the doctors would have detected hemochromatosis, and he could have avoided advanced organ damage. As it is, this affluent gentleman spent a lot of money each year on a health exam, while the disease that ended up being his real problem remained undetected. So much for the benefit of having an annual exam.

The current practice of annual exams varies a great deal. Physical exam findings in asymptomatic people are rarely positive. A carefully taken history , one including the entire family history, might be more fruitful. The great Canadian physician, William Osler, emphasized repeatedly the value of the history in making a diagnosis over the value of the results of a physical examination. So again, we might question the use of Pap smears and mammograms for most adult women. We have pointed out some reservations about the value of mammography, particularly when the adverse effects of false positive studies are considered in the total yield picture.

Most physicians go through the motions of performing a physical examination. Despite the small yield of the physical examination, it is done because lay people expect to be examined and accept the "laying on of hands" philosophy. A typical annual examination includes running batteries of hematological (i.e., blood) tests as well as a chemistry battery. The yield is quite small in patients without symptoms, however. Instead, physicians should point out the effects of lifestyle choices, which truly determine a patient's health. Smokers should strongly be urged to quit smoking. Obese patients should be advised to lose weight. The latter should be advised to exercise. Several patient care studies have revealed that physicians rarely recommended smoking cessation and weight loss to patients during an annual examination. The attitude appears to be that these problems are already obvious to the patient and that it is pointless to bring up a potentially delicate or uncomfortable subject. Physicians often want to be popular with their patients, and they may think that bringing up a painful subject would be hazardous and without value. And yet studies indicate that a physician's advice to quit smoking is as good a stimulus as any in convincing a patient to cease. The yield is less apparent with obesity, but at least the physician could point out the health hazards of being overweight, so that the patient may be stimulated to start a weight reduction regimen. These factors will be covered in greater detail in this chapter.

Much of what occurs in the annual health evaluation appears to be medical busywork, although a few disorders might be detected early. Studies evaluating the yield of the annual exam found benefits to be woefully lacking. [3] This is the reason why national organizations have expressed serious doubts about the value of having annual exams, unless the exam is selective. Early detection of hypertension and diabetes is valuable, because these diseases are asymptomatic in their early stages and yet can cause organ damage if not detected early. Taking a careful medical history may also help physicians improve the yield of the annual physical. The value of the physical examination, beyond the benefits of blood pressure measurement, is doubtful.

THE COMPRESSION OF MORBIDITY

My view on the relative lack of value of periodic health examinations, particularly in the elderly, was crystalized by a recent study by James Fries, a well-regarded researcher from Stanford University. [4] Dr. Fries is also famous for his support of the theoretical concept of the life span (a topic covered earlier). Fries' study compared longevity and disability in two population groups comprised of graduates of the University of Pennsylvania. Despite the obvious "selection" compromise in this study, statisticians support the study because the comparison end points were so distinct. The study examined what Fries called "compression of morbidity," a theoretical term referring to the shortened time period of illness or disability prior to death. Most people would agree that experiencing a shortened period (i.e., a "compression") prior to death is preferable to suffering through a prolonged illness, with its discomfort and disability. In fact, elderly people who are reasonably well often prefer dying in their sleep without any period of illness. A famous author, George Bernard Shaw, desired this kind of death, stating that he hoped "to be knifed in the back by a jealous husband." This of course did not happen; G.B.S. broke his hip at age ninety-one and died of complications. The desire that we have a short period of feeling well before death rather than a longer period of sickness is Fries' "compression of morbidity."

One group in the study, described as the "clean livers," had a desirable lifestyle, in which they didn't smoke cigarettes, they maintained a normal body weight, and they exercised regularly. The other group—"dissolute livers," if you will—smoked cigarettes, were overweight, and were the proverbial "couch potatoes." No other health factors were included in the comparison. The results were informative. Longevity was only slightly longer in the "clean livers," suggesting that lifestyle patterns do not necessarily increase life expectancy. However, the terminal disability of the "clean livers" was notably less intense and compressed into fewer years. In summary, Fries' "compression of morbidity" is accomplished by a healthier lifestyle.

If this study is believed—and it "makes sense"—we might ask just how feasible compression of morbidity is for people to achieve? In theory, very, but in practice probably not very. Most people do not choose a particular lifestyle in order to achieve "compression of morbidity" before their exit. This kind of thinking is not typical. People have different lifestyles for complex reasons, not often including that they desire "compression of morbidity." At any rate, some of the lifestyle factors needed to compress morbidity are difficult to attain. As we will demonstrate, obese people tend to remain obese. Regular exercise is simply not something a lot of people want to do. Quitting cigarette smoking is clearly possible, as the major successes in particular population groups show, but it is still difficult. Despite pointing out these difficulties, Fries' study yields important lessons about preventive medicine. What counts is physicians recommending the hard work of "clean living," not going through the busywork practiced in the annual health evaluation.

YIELD OF THE ANNUAL PHYSICAL

As we have already strongly suggested, it is hard to demonstrate a significant yield in health benefits from the annual health evaluation. It may well be that the most a physician can accomplish in a periodic health evaluation is pointing out that a better lifestyle offers more value to the health of the patient than the busywork of the annual checkup. Perhaps practitioners prefer not to describe the parts of their practice that cover office overhead as "busywork." Let's discuss in more detail a few of the issues physicians can address when visiting with patients.

OBESITY

This nation, and almost all of the Western democracies, are in the midst of an obesity epidemic.[5] The epidemic started a bit later in Western Europe, but nevertheless, it now parallels ours. The epidemic is only about twenty years old, a time during which the number of overweight adults has doubled. Childhood obesity has tripled in incidence, causing medical problems hitherto limited to adults. In some minority populations, almost half of the children are overweight.

Weight control has been covered abundantly by the media over the past several years. Legitimate concerns about the increase of obesity-related diseases challenge the advances achieved by medical technology.[6] In other words, the small yield obtained by advances in medicine, created at tremendous expense, may be canceled out by the obesity epidemic. The medical costs of people with obesity are 40 percent higher than in persons of normal weight.[7] An obese Medicare patient costs fifteen hundred dollars more annually than a non-obese patient.

Not only does obesity cost the nation more, but the recently accomplished small increases in life expectancies of obese people may be reversed if the epidemic continues on its current path. Current estimates indicate that two thirds of Americans are overweight or obese. The portion of those with extreme obesity has increased at an especially rapid rate. These trends have affected all social groups, although the largest increases have been demonstrated in children and minorities. A recent estimate is that three hundred thousand deaths occur each year because of obesity.

The loss of years of life attributed to obesity has been quantified.[8] Even a moderate amount of excess weight reduces life expectancy. As the degree of overweight increases, a prominent contraction of life expectancy occurs. This pattern is more apparent in white people; moderate levels of obesity in black people reduce life expectancy to a lesser degree. The greatest reduction in life expectancy occurs when the obesity begins in the very young. One often cited example is that of a twenty-year-old white male with severe obesity who may have lost as much as 20 percent of his potential life expectancy.

Physician Disinterest in Obesity

Considering the health and longevity implications of obesity, why do physicians appear so disinterested in its correction? Along with stopping smoking, losing weight is one way a person can prevent future illness. The problem may be somewhat similar to the "disinterest" physicians appear to have in nutrition. Unfortunately, obesity is a real hazard to health and should be addressed, whereas nutritional deficiency in everyday practice is virtually non-existent. Perhaps as a result of this apparent disinterest, obesity correction is predominantly a commercial activity, consisting of weight control salons, commercial clinics, over-the-counter diet preparations, constant articles on weight loss in ladies' journals, etc. One estimate suggests that obesity correction is a forty-billion-dollar-a-year industry. Astoundingly this industry has flourished while obesity has flourished. How on earth can we spend so much money on an effort which continues to fail? Most businesses would fail if they could not achieve better results. Commercial purveyors of weight control might suggest that the obesity epidemic would be worse if not for their efforts. If you believe this, you might be interested in purchasing a piece of the Brooklyn Bridge that I have for sale...!

Why, indeed, are physicians relatively uninvolved in obesity control? The economics of modern medical practice is a major factor. It is simply not feasible for physicians to spend the time necessary to counsel a patient on the importance and details of weight loss. A physician who must see five or six patients an hour in office practice does not have the time to deal with weight loss. All the physician can do is point out to the patient the health hazards of being overweight and refer the patient to a weight loss clinic.

The second and possibly more important reason for lack of physician involvement is psychological. Physicians are human and have a legitimate desire to see their efforts yield fruit. And they also like to see their medical efforts bear fruit sooner rather than later. Experience with weight loss has historically been so unrewarding and unsuccessful that physicians may elect to remain uninvolved. Only two or three percent of people can maintain weight loss over a period of a few years. If the physician were actively involved, these failures could be viewed as her or his fault.

Health Consequences of Obesity

Obesity is not conducive to a long life. It shortens life by increasing a person's chance of developing a host of diseases directly related to the obesity.[9]

Cardiovascular disease, contributed to by the increased incidence of hypertension and blood lipid abnormalities in obesity, is the major condition increasing mortality and morbidity in overweight people. Type 2 diabetes mellitus is dramatically increased in obese people, contributing to the development of even more cardiovascular, renal, and eye diseases. Strokes are also more common in overweight persons. The benign conditions exaggerated by obesity are osteoarthritis (i.e., the wear-and-tear of cartilage in weight-bearing joints) and gallstones. Certain cancers, notably endometrial cancer (i.e., cancer of the uterus lining) and breast cancer are increased in obese women.

Cause of Obesity

Is the tendency to obesity inherited or does it have an environmental cause? The long-standing debate about the etiology (or cause) of obesity has lessened because of the current obesity epidemic. As in most controversial subjects, a bit of both is probably true. Very clearly, environment is a huge causation factor; we know this because the epidemic is of recent origin. Our genes have not changed in the past twenty years.

There undoubtedly are inherited predispositions to become overweight. Biological variation is the rule in any species; why would the incidence of obesity not be variable in people? Some people who are "skinny as a rail" appear to eat constantly and yet remain very thin. Others who are overweight despite "not eating enough to keep a bird alive" represents the other extreme. These observations can be misleading, however. When thin people are interviewed carefully about their eating habits and food interests, one may find that they are relatively disinterested in food and eating. They may not eat as much as they believe or as much as others think they do. They often are disciplined persons who never snack between meals. They often are fussy eaters who do not "clean their plates." They may eat desserts rarely. Junk food may have little appeal for the thin person. On the other hand, heavy people who insist that they eat very little, often eat a lot more than they admit. When their food intake is quantitated, they find that they consume more than they realize. They enjoy eating, and may actually discuss the next meal when they are finishing the current meal.

Considering much of the above, it must be apparent that the current environment of available high calorie food and the reduced expenditure of calories in work and play combine to create an imbalance of consumption and expenditure of food energy. So blaming the current epidemic entirely or even largely on inheritance is putting our respective heads in the sand. People simply are eating more food than their bodies require.

Epidemiology of Obesity

Certain variables contribute to the obesity epidemic which may be instructive to those interested in the phenomenon.

Age

Weight gain is normal in adults. The gain occurs in non-overweight people as well as those who are overweight. This normal weight gain may in part be due to the expected slowing down of our metabolism as we age. There can be no doubt that the young expend more energy than those of us in advanced years. This normal biological feature contributes to weight gain, particularly because our eating habits do not seem to change. If anything, the enjoyment of eating may increase as the passions of youth subside. Although weight gain normally occurs slowly throughout life, the most rapid weight gain occurs in the twenties. There are probably some psychological explanations for this observation, but they are unknown.

Gender

Obesity is significantly more common in women than men. Despite this fact, women are less prone to the medical complications of obesity than are men. These factors contribute to the longer life expectancy of women than men. Any casual observation of nursing homes or assisted care facilities will note that there are a lot more women than men, a fact only partially accounted for by increased life expectancy. In fact, many elderly women are distinctly overweight and yet achieve advanced age. Fat old men are a rarity.

Part of the difference in the medical complications of men and women are related to their fat distribution. The male body classically has a prominent abdomen (a pot belly, if you will), small butt, and spindly legs. The kind of fat which is most prominent in this distribution within the abdomen is called "visceral."[10] Visceral fat is metabolically different that subcutaneous fat (i.e., fat in the skin) and the difference explains why men suffer more from abnormal lipids than women.

Women, on the other hand, have small abdomens, with prominent hips and thighs (they are pear-shape, if you will) and the increased adipose tissue is in the subcutaneous fat. If a woman has more of a male body type, presumably with more visceral fat, she will have the health hazards of men. Conversely, if a man has a pear-shape with lower body fat accumulations, he will suffer less complications of obesity than most males.

Race

Black people differ significantly from white people both in obesity incidence and its medical significance. Black men have about the same incidence of being overweight as white men. More of a black man's weight is muscle when compared to that of white men. Black women, on the other hand, have a striking incidence of obesity, almost twice as high as that of white women. Current estimates indicate that as many as 80 percent of black women are overweight or obese.

The high incidence of obesity in black women could be related to socio-economic factors; blacks tend to be in the lower socio-economic levels of society, in which obesity is clearly more common. While this may be partially true, it does not explain the phenomenon completely. Obesity is equally common in poor and affluent black women, a parallel not found between populations of white women.

Two additional reasons have been proposed for the high incidence of obesity in black women, one psychological and one cultural. Black women, it is suggested, accept being overweight and place little emphasis on the value of being thin. Measures of personal self-esteem confirm that obese black women are perfectly comfortable with their size. This level of comfort does not exist in a great many white women, for whom being thin is a major concern and desire. Eating disorders are rare in black women; anorexia and bulimia occur almost entirely in young white women.

The second reason for obesity in black women may be cultural. Being overweight is often considered satisfactory and normal among black people. When a black man looks at an obese black woman, he may describe her as a "big person," if he comments at all. On the other hand, a white man would describe an obese white woman as "fat," a distinctly more pejorative description.

The more important aspect of obesity in black women relates to their relative freedom from the negative health consequences of obesity.

Overweight or mildly obese black women have no obvious increase in the medical consequences of obesity. Only when black women become very obese do the hazards of obesity manifest. A result of this apparent level of protection is the inability of black women to successfully diet. After all, if you are psychologically comfortable with being overweight and also are not medically harmed, why bother?

Socio-Economic Differences

Levels of obesity differ dramatically with levels of affluence or education. The poor have high levels of obesity, both in men and women. The affluent and more highly educated people place more emphasis on being of normal weight. Some of this is financial. High-calorie foods, such as are served in the fast-food establishments, cost less than the seafoods, fruits, and vegetables preferred by the rich and educated.

Another interesting variable about the attitudes of a particular population group towards being overweight is present in young men of any race. Although young white females are often concerned about being overweight, at times to the point of having eating disorders, young men often consider being muscular and large (or actually fat) as desirably macho. Even though their weight defines them as being overweight or obese, they may be emotionally comfortable. Unfortunately, since heavy young men become heavier older men, and have the attendant health consequences, this attitude is self-defeating in the long run.

Inheritance

We have already minimized the importance of genetics in the current obesity epidemic. Nevertheless, family patterns exist, suggesting some element of inheritance. Eighty percent of children from two obese parents will be obese as adults. Only 20 percent of children of two lean parents will suffer future obesity. Separating the environmental social habits of eating from genetics is difficult. Heavy parents often want their children to eat well. Slender parents often desire their children to be thin.

Definition of Obesity

The current standard of appropriate weight is the body mass index (BMI).

$$BMI = \frac{\text{weight in kg}}{\text{height in meters}^2}$$

The BMI is defined in metric terms; English parameters in pounds and inches are available. The ranges of abnormal and normal BMI values are as follows:

Underweight = < 20	Normal = 20 – 25
Overweight = 25 – 30	Obese = > 30
Severely obese = > 40	Morbidly obese = > 50

Being underweight is theoretically valuable because some of the medical consequences of obesity are further reduced. However, many of the underweight have other disorders. Therefore, having a low BMI is less desirable than it might appear. The value of the BMI is its reproducibility and direct correlation with the medical conditions adversely affecting health. An increase in health consequences increases exponentially with increasing BMI. The major advantage of the BMI is its simplicity; height and weight are objective. We thus avoid depending on "body build" differences, which are subjective and susceptible to interpretation.

Pediatric Obesity

The dramatic increase in childhood obesity in the past twenty to thirty years has stimulated abundant commentary in the media and healthcare circles. It is widely recognized that overweight children nearly always become obese adults with all the adverse health consequences. We senior citizens rarely recall seeing overweight kids in our younger years. Most children were thin, with parents always trying to fatten them up. (We now know this encouragement to be in error because thinness in children is healthy.) Children with severe obesity now develop a condition formerly limited to adults, type 2 diabetes mellitus.

In fact, type 2 diabetes was once called maturity-onset diabetes, a reflection of its age range. Previously, we thought that the worst fate for overweight or obese children was being ridiculed by their peers. The problem is now recognized as much more serious.

The cause of the epidemic of obesity in children is clear: it has the same etiology as the adult condition. Children now consume too many food calories and burn up fewer calories in play and other activities. We often see children walking about with a can of soda pop and a package of chips in their hands, as early as the morning. In my younger days, soda pop was a Sunday dinner treat, if we were fortunate. Instead of outdoor sports, children spend many hours watching television or using electronic games. These couch potato activities further contribute to snack consumption. For reasons unclear to me, plumpness in children is not always criticized by adults who believe it is simply a manifestation of their child's young age. After all, the kids do not appear to be ill. Thinking of future weight-related health issues is rarely a concern of parents. The children consume the same high-calorie snack foods that their overweight parents consume.

The major concern in pediatric obesity is the prediction of adult obesity. Being able to predict adult obesity in kids varies somewhat with the age of the child. For neonates under one year, obesity is only slightly predictive of adult obesity. Obesity in elementary school children, ages six to eleven, is moderately predictive. In adolescents ages eleven to fifteen pediatric obesity is very predictive of future adult obesity. Almost 100 percent of severely obese adults were overweight as adolescents. Therefore, efforts to control pediatric obesity should be directed primarily at young teen-agers. Unfortunately, this age group includes children who rarely seek medical attention. Because of this, the responsibility becomes a parental one. Effecting change in young teen-agers is a monumental task. They feel well and cannot understand the stress on weight control, beyond its effect on clothing selection and sports participation. Solely from an historical viewpoint, I fear that the epidemic of obesity will continue, in part because insufficient stress is given to the predictive consequences of obesity for children.

Psychology of Obesity

Being obese presents many obvious handicaps to the overweight individual. We have already stressed the health compromises of being overweight, namely increased morbidity (i.e., disease) and decreased longevity. Society inflicts its own pain and discomfort on obese people. Generally, being heavy is socially unacceptable; we label heavy people as lazy, slovenly, indifferent, etc. Obese people are also compromised in employment opportunities. Potential employers often view an obese prospective employee as lazy and unlikely to be a strong performer. Even the prospect of marriage unions is compromised, particularly for women. Our society generally venerates slender people. As a result, an obese woman has finite limits in attracting a mate. Further, if she is successful in attracting a male, she may be limited to a man of modest financial and social class attributes. Finally, clothing selection is limited for obese people, although clothing manufactures are recognizing the growing number of heavy persons. Stores catering to heavy customers are now more widespread.

Considering all the negative attributes and handicaps of being obese, one cannot help but wonder why people permit themselves to become and remain heavy. What appears obvious in our superficial evaluation is surely far more complex psychologically for the obese person.

Perhaps the common denominator of the maintenance of the condition is "acceptance." Overweight people did not wake up one morning and discover that they were overweight. The weight increase occurred over a period of many years, beginning perhaps as early as in the teen years. Weight gain is largely imperceptible. Many heavy people cannot recall any time in their lives when they were not heavier than their peers and so they accept being overweight as part of who they are.

Part of just "accepting" one's weight is refusing to think about it or to consider the problem. The thought of changing one's dietary habits or actively dieting to lose weight is overwhelmingly painful. After all, eating is enjoyable; eating less in any dietary regimen is woefully unpleasant. A great many obese people have a history of attempting to lose weight, each time with short-lived success. The discomfort of dieting was gradually alleviated by resuming excessive eating, so much so that they gain back more weight than they lost on the diet. In time, the "acceptance" results in an attitude of "I've always been fat and I will stay that way."

Many people do not believe that they are overweight, despite the fact that their BMI places them in the overweight or obese category. We have mentioned adult black women for whom being heavy is relatively psychologically and culturally acceptable. A similar exception occurs with young men who believe that a few extra pounds is a "macho" phenomenon. And people are less likely to change if they consider themselves to be an appropriate weight.

Losing weight is very uncomfortable. Although the vendors of weight loss regimens claim that their method is pain-free, that is far from the truth. Weight loss is starvation and starvation is inherently uncomfortable. And so people avoid dieting. Another contributor to "accepting" oneself as an overweight person is the tendency to believe that the changes in morbidity and mortality do not apply to them. This ostrich-like thinking is similarly common in cigarette smokers who say, "It won't happen to me." Another factor of "acceptance" may be simple ignorance. When obese people develop health problems they don't see being overweight as the cause. They blame their heart disease on hypertension or coronary disease, without admitting that their predisposition to those disorders was caused by obesity. Indeed, obesity is an overwhelming problem to many. An obese person's "acceptance" may predispose him or her to not addressing it with action.

Therapy of Obesity

A major challenge to correcting obesity is that efforts often fail. As few as 2 or 3 percent of obese people lose weight and maintain their weight loss. Almost any dietary attempt is successful at weight loss, but only for a short period. Heavy people gained weight over many years, and committing oneself to the restrictions involved in weight loss requires years of unpleasant activity. One's lifestyle must change and this is particularly difficult for overweight people. The body's reaction to any weight loss regimen is counterproductive. When we lose weight—

starve may be a better term—the body's metabolism slows to conserve energy and reduce the pace of weight loss. This slowing of the metabolism persists when the person resumes a normal diet, so that the "normal" diet is excessive for the individual's metabolic needs. Everything works against successful weight loss, and our experience confirms how difficult achieving normal weight can be.

RECOMMENDATIONS

Not every overweight person should attempt to achieve a normal BMI. A plump black woman will not suffer the medical consequences of being overweight and should have much less concern about achieving a normal BMI. On the other hand, overweight young men should be told that they have the genuine risk of becoming obese older men, with all the medical consequences involved. Similarly, heavy teen-agers should know that they most likely will become obese adults, again with all its negative aspects. Elderly women who are moderately heavy and still feel well should have much less concern about being heavy. The simple fact that they are female and have survived to advanced age should be sufficient evidence that their weight is not a medical concern. At their age, eating may be one of the few remaining pleasures. It would be unkind or even criminal to put them on a weight-reducing regimen.

SMOKING & HEALTH

By this time, the reader should be absolutely convinced that cigarette smoking is a major hazard to one's health and that cessation of smoking may be the most fruitful ingredient in preventive medicine. Of all the activities practiced in preventive medicine, cessation of smoking may be both the easiest to achieve and by far the most productive to better health.

The history of tobacco use, particularly cigarette smoking, is relatively recent in the United States and the other Western democracies.[11] Smoking was almost entirely a male activity until around World

War I. And prior to World War I, men smoked predominately cigars and pipes, which typically involved less inhalation. The environment of trench warfare in World War I made pipe smoking inconvenient, thereby leading to an increase in cigarette smoking. The increased manufacture of already-rolled cigarettes further contributed to expanded use. As a result of these historical factors, lung cancer, perhaps the most important health hazard of smoking, was a rare disease until after World War I. Alton Ochsner, the famous Tulane surgeon, saw an autopsy of a lung cancer patient in 1919 and was told by the pathologist that he might never see this pathology again. How wrong the pathologist was! By 1936, just seventeen years later, Ochsner attended the autopsies of nine lung cancer patients in only six months. The lung cancer epidemic had begun!

American male smoking increased dramatically during World War II. Free cigarettes were included in C and K rations for GIs overseas. Stateside, cigarettes in military bases were almost given away. One might suggest that the "generous" cigarette companies were fully aware of the addictive power of cigarettes; their generosity may represent clever marketing. Studies have indicated that nicotine in cigarettes is far more addictive than are heroin or cocaine. Those trying to quit smoking cigarettes know all too well the addictive properties of nicotine.

During World War II, and in the period following, women took up cigarette smoking in significant numbers. Prior to this time women smokers were frowned upon. Part of "women's liberation" unfortunately involved the freedom to take up a bad, previously male-only habit. The Surgeon General report in 1964 on the health hazards of smoking did not deter the continuation of smoking in women. The cigarette manufacturers, reacting to the growing health concerns about smoking, introduced filter cigarettes in 1952, ostensibly to reduce inhalation of cancer causing substances. Kent cigarettes originally used a filter made of asbestos, a substance now incriminated in a host of pulmonary diseases. Subsequent studies of the value of filter cigarettes demonstrated no reduction of disease due to the filters. Their use was strictly a marketing ploy, designed to create a false sense of security. But for the public, it "made sense" that filters were beneficial.

Cigarette promotions specifically targeted at women began with Virginia Slims ads in 1979. Their motto, "You've come a long way, baby," was a poorly disguised attempt to equate smoking with women's liberation. It would appear that the marketing effort was successful.

Sociological patterns in cigarette smoking have changed in interesting ways over the past two to three decades. The increased incidences of lung cancer and a host of other related diseases has paralleled the increase in cigarette smoking. Because the practice started later in women, they are twenty years behind men in lung cancer mortality. However, women are now on a parallel course of lung cancer incidence and there is some statistical suggestion that women are more susceptible to lung cancer than are men.

Because of the obvious health hazards of smoking, some segments of the population have reduced their use. Although smoking in both sexes has decreased, the decrease is more impressive in men. Smoking in teenagers has decreased, but to a lesser degree. Amongst teens, smoking is highest in girls. Smoking has become an increasingly "blue collar" habit, much less common in affluent or educated people. Cigarette smoking in physicians decreased from over 60 percent in the '60s to less than 5 percent today. Smoking in medical students is rare.

Drs. Doll and Peto, world-renowned Oxford University epidemiologists, have recently reported an important quantitative evaluation of the health hazards of cigarette smoking. Their study of smoking in British physicians began in 1951, concluding in 2001, constituting a monumental fifty-year study of the morbidity and mortality attributed directly to cigarette smoking. They began the study with thirty-five thousand physicians in 1951, of whom 80 percent were regular smokers, a figure not too dissimilar to that describing American physicians at that time. Their study not only examined the excess mortality caused by smoking, but it also quantitated the improvement in life expectancy created by stopping smoking at different ages.

The major conclusion of the fifty-year study was that physicians who did not quit smoking lost ten years of life. If they did quit smoking during the study period, the loss of life expectancy lessened, depending on their age when they ceased. Even stopping at age sixty decreased the loss of life expectancy. The study also confirmed that half of all regular smokers will die of diseases directly related to the smoking habit. The Doll and Peto study pointed out an even more ominous problem for current cigarette smokers. The age of onset of smoking initiation has decreased over the study period. Whereas smokers once took up the habit in adulthood, most now start in the teen years. This earlier initiation of smoking creates an additional burden of damage, such that the current generation of smokers will face an even higher excess of early disease and mortality.

People have created a health demon. Smoking is a frightful habit with no redeeming health features. Smoking cessation is by far the most important public health initiative of our time; 90 percent of the associated diseases can be avoided by quitting smoking. As a public health problem, counseling against it is the most fruitful preventive medicine method available to physicians. Whereas correction of obesity has an enduring success rate of 2 or 3 percent, a very high percentage of smokers can and do quit. Physicians have a real role in encouraging cessation, but unfortunately, physicians often take on this role only after significant disease has occurred. A few minutes of encouragement by physicians would be far more fruitful in preventing disease than the routine laboratory and imaging procedures now utilized under the guise of delivering "preventive medicine."

SUMMARY

The lay public generally accepts the thesis that having annual health evaluations will increase one's longevity and the quality of health. The theoretical rationale is to detect diseases earlier, when therapy is allegedly more successful. Although the concept "makes sense," what "makes sense" must withstand the scrutiny of validation by random clinical trials, as we pointed out in the section on evidence-based medicine. To a great extent, such evidence is hard to come by.

Many major health organizations have agreed that the annual physical, as it is currently done, has scant yield and should be abandoned in favor of a more selective health evaluation. Although the public desires a physical examination in their annual health evaluation, the yield in disease detection is very small. Similarly, batteries of laboratory tests and routine x-rays rarely find abnormalities in asymptomatic patients. Physicians should point out the importance of lifestyle choices instead of having the patient go through a physical exam and multiple "tests." For patients the most obvious choices are to quit smoking and achieve a normal body weight.

Fries' "compression of morbidity," provides support for holding that a better lifestyle improves one's health. Although "clean living" increases longevity only slightly, those individuals "living cleanly" had shorter and less severe terminal illnesses.

The current epidemic of obesity in the Western world has the potential of cancelling the advances achieved by modern medical technology by increasing obesity-related diseases. Not only will medical progress be reduced, but the increased care costs created by obesity will further exacerbate healthcare inflation. Unfortunately, obesity correction is more an unrealized hope than a realistic accomplishment. Although the current epidemic affects all groups of our population, the adverse effects on health are more prominent in men. Similarly, although obesity is prevalent in black women, they are relatively unaffected unless the obesity level is severe. The importance of the obesity problem in children relates entirely to its prediction of adult obesity.

Cigarette smoking is by far the most serious health hazard. Humankind has indeed created a monster in the past century. Cigarette smoking contributes to a host of serious diseases, including many cancers. The magnificent fifty-year study of smoking in British physicians by Doll and Peto provides evidence of a quantitative loss of life expectancy due to smoking. The study also clearly demonstrates the importance of cessation at any age. In contrast to those trying to lose weight, many people quit smoking, particularly those of higher income and education levels. Physicians have a real role in helping people quit smoking, and should spend the time instead of doing the medical "busywork" now involved in the current annual health examination.

References

1. S. K. Oboler, et al, "Public Expectations and Attitudes for Annual Physical Examinations," *Ann Int Med* 136 (2002): 652-9.

2. Oboler, et al, "Public Expectations and Attitudes," 652-9.

3. H. G. Welch, "Right and Wrong Reasons to Be Screened," *Ann Int Med* 140, No 9 (May 4, 2004): 784-7.

4. J. F. Fries, "Aging, Cumulative Disability, and the Compression of Morbidity," *Comp Ther* 27, No. 4 (2001): 322-29.

5. K. M. Flegal and M. D. Carroll, "Prevalence and Trends in Obseity Among US Adults, 1999-2000," *JAMA* 288, No. 14 (October 9, 2002): 1723-26.

6. S. J. Olshansky, et al, "A Potential Decline in Life Expectancy in the U.S. in the 21st Century," *N Eng J Med* 352, No 11 (March 17, 2005): 1138-45.

7. Finkelstein, et al, "State-Level Estimates of Annual Medical Expenditures Attributable to Obesity" Vol. 12, No. 1 (January 2004): 18-24.

8. K. R., Fontaine, "Years of Life Lost Due to Obesity," *JAMA* 289, No 2 (January 8, 2003): 193-97.

9. B. T. Burton and W. R. Foster, "Health Implications of Obesity," *J Am Dietetic Assn* 85 No. 9 (September 1985): 1117-21.

10. A. N. Peiris, M. S. Sothmann, et al, "Adiposity, Fat Distribution, and Cardiovascular Risk," *Ann Int Med* 110 (1989): 867-72.

11. M. C. Fiore, "Trends in Cigarette Smoking in the U.S.," *Med Clin N America* 76, No 2 (March 1992): 289-303.

Conclusions & Recommendations

By this time, you may have concluded that your author is far from pleased with the American healthcare system. The system suffers from mediocre quality and overwhelming cost inflation. If the system exhibited better quality, the cost inflation would be acceptable. In comparison with other Western democracies, we simply do not receive benefits in a proportion commensurate with the costs incurred. Although Americans believe chauvinistically that our health system is the best in the world, the evidence points otherwise. Citizens in other nations, particularly those with nationalized healthcare systems, also believe theirs is best. They also believe their care is free. They pay as well, however, through taxes rather than private or governmental insurance premiums. Although we may have somewhat better facilities and an ability to obtain elective care promptly, we don't have better long-term outcomes in terms of longevity and quality than have other nations.

These comments don't amount to an endorsement of the nationalized health systems now in place in many Western nations. Their method of reducing costs is to restrict funding of medical care. Whenever money is short, health financing is reduced. Elective surgery is delayed, causing patients to wait many months to be scheduled. Some of the delay may reduce costs by resulting in the premature deaths of patients who don't receive life-saving interventions. Some of the delay and other restrictions prevent appropriate diagnostic procedures for cancer, thus also reducing cost. Still, despite the delay and overt rationing of care, one would be hard put to demonstrate that care outcomes are compromised ultimately. Mortality data for heart disease and cancer outcomes are similar throughout the Western democracies, however the health system is financed.

The almost exponential cost inflation of healthcare in the United States over the past several decades has created problems in our economy. Resources expended on healthcare are not available for other

173

public activities. Labor-management problems currently involve health insurance benefits. Older businesses which once offered generous health benefits to employees now are competitively handicapped by younger companies not offering equivalent health insurance benefits and pensions.

A major contributor to cost inflation is our increasingly procedure-oriented technology. The public may be overly impressed by technology, but the technology-dependent activities must be useful to patient care, not simply impressive. A great deal of modern technology is duplicative; it is excessive and isn't necessary. Physicians in an earlier era were quite capable of arriving at accurate diagnoses without depending on expensive procedures. Instead of ordering batteries of laboratory tests and imaging procedures, physicians used their medical training and intellect to arrive at diagnoses. Part of this procedure-oriented care is created by lay people's unrealistic expectations of the value of testing as compared to thoughtful hands-on diagnosis. The common expectation is to depend on more tests rather than on the physician's cognitive abilities.

I am amazed at the several proposals to control healthcare inflation. Most of the activities are financial and administrative, and they don't address the more basic question of patient benefit. The public believes that more healthcare and medical research will prolong life expectancies and improve quality. The belief that there should be no spending limit for modern medical technology flourishes. Unfortunately, as has been pointed out, our society may be approaching the limits of life expectancy; we are predestined to live a finite number of years, no matter how much medical care can accomplish. Certain population groups are now approaching this finite life span. Spending more money to improve life expectancies will require an inordinate resource expenditure, and with very modest gain.

The above should not imply that progress in medical science is not impressive. On the contrary, much of the most important progress is in basic medical science, which is absolutely required for future progress in disease management. The media contribute to unrealistic expectations of what these basic advances will offer in the near future. Translating the knowledge gained in basic science into everyday patient care will take many years. Certain fields in medicine have made impressive contributions to the quality of life of people. Orthopedics, ophthalmology, and cardiology have yielded major care advances, making life better for elderly individuals. Whether these advances prolong life is debatable. Although of obvious value to selected patients, these therapies contribute significantly to our healthcare cost inflation.

My views on healthcare are pessimistic. I have doubts about our ability to control healthcare inflation without the heavy hand of government. My preference would be to educate the public and members of the medical profession about the true gains of using expensive healthcare activities, so that care will become commensurate with the costs spent on care. There was a time when healthcare was available at reasonable costs. Physicians should be quite capable of taking care of their patients without breaking the bank. A great deal of care is given to patients for self-limited illnesses. Physicians should be capable of recognizing these self-limited conditions, and with appropriate patient education, hopefully the public will accept a physician's recommendation that time will provide the cure. Unfortunately, this approach runs up against the American personality that emphasizes action rather than inaction. The American way is bigger, better, and faster, and these requirements contribute to cost inflation. The classic example of excessive care for a self-limited disorder is prescribing antibiotics for viral upper-respiratory infections. With no evidence that the patient's illness will be improved by expensive antibiotics, doctors nevertheless prescribe these drugs to great excess. Does every person with a stomach ache require a CT scan or MRI? What did physicians of an earlier era do in similar circumstances? And did patient care suffer? Probably not.

As pointed out in my chapter on "cancer progress," despite tremendous oncology expenditures, reduction in both incidence and mortality from cancer is unchanged compared to the past. Even if we could attain "progress," the longevity yields would be small. If every cancer were curable, life expectancy would increase only 2.3 years. Modern cancer chemotherapy is frightfully expensive, involving new medications that cost thousands of dollars. Therapy for recurrent cancers is excessive. Instead of providing symptomatic comfort, oncologists continue chemotherapy long after any improvement is possible. Oncologists seem to refuse to consider the admonition that "the tumor determines the outcome, not the care." In addition to recommending excessive futile care, physicians recommend routinely cancer followup procedures without apparent indication. There is scant evidence that earlier detection of recurrent disease is any more effective than waiting until the tumor makes itself known.

How do we turn around the thinking of the lay public about the long-term value of healthcare? This is a very difficult task. In effect, the lay public has been educated to believe that one should go to the doctor when one is ill and one should go to the doctor regularly for a health evaluation. The latter should be readily addressed. Since major medical organizations no longer extol the value of the annual physical as it is currently carried out, insurance companies should have ample justification to reduce coverage for the annual exam. Instead of a comprehensive exam, replete with laboratory and imaging testing, the exam should be selective and inexpensive, looking for abnormalities worth treating. Epidemiologists should make firm recommendations about which part of the annual exam should be retained, if any. We should consider age and gender in deciding the extent of the annual exam. For example, why do we waste time and money doing health evaluations on eighty and ninety-year old women in nursing homes or assistive care facilities? Their age proves their durability and longevity. If they have no symptoms, leave them alone. Performing lipid blood studies on 90-year-old women in nursing homes is ridiculous, if not actually inhumane. If we wasted less resources on useless screening tests in very old patients, perhaps more money would be available to provide basic creature comforts to our seniors.

The public should be taught that not every upper respiratory infection requires medical care. Educating the public on self-limited diseases may be a formidable task. The public prefers to transfer responsibility for their health to physicians, even when adopting a better lifestyle would be far more effective. If education does not work, the second best approach would be reducing insurance coverage for self-limited conditions. Physician education about the anticipated yield of ancillary diagnostic testing might reduce the cost contribution of tests without demonstrable yields. Do we really require a CT scan or MRI study for every instance of trauma? Most traumatic injuries heal, with or without medical care.

Another proposed approach to cost reduction is to retain primary care responsibilities for family physicians, so that specialists and subspecialists are less involved in everyday health problems. We should return to the "captain of the ship" philosophy, in which primary care physicians retain ultimate responsibility for medical decisions. Keeping the patient out of the hands of the expensive specialists would both improve care and save money. A variety of approaches would be required to maintain the primary care role in medical care. The trend to office-only practice should be discouraged. Primary care physicians, despite believing it an "inefficient" use of their time, should make rounds on their hospitalized patients. The movement to hospitalists, another economic innovation, should be discouraged. If primary care physicians regularly attended their hospitalized patients, they could more readily attend continuing medical education conferences. Much of the above defies the current economic and "efficient" practice styles which are driven by financial concerns.

Another radical approach is to involve physicians personally in the costs incurred by excessive care. If physicians were penalized for ordering unindicated tests or rewarded for requiring fewer tests, some semblance of cost control could be attained. As it is, physicians incur no responsibility for the tests and procedures they order; insurance picks up the tab.

Other cost savings could accrue from greater FDA control of dietary supplements. The DSHEA should be retracted, giving the FDA jurisdiction over the efficacy and safety of supplements. In a similar manner, unsupported claims about the benefits of complementary and alternative care (CAM) should require evidence of both efficacy and safety. Finally, direct-to-consumer (DTC) advertising, almost entirely an American innovation, should be banned.

Implementing all of the above would require a major expansion of federal government oversight, hopefully providing significant cost savings and at the same time contributing to quality of care. Many would resists these suggestions. CAM advocates and purveyors would object to the requirement for proof of the value of their activities. Devoted consumers of dietary supplements would object from a consumerism viewpoint. The pharmaceutical industry would scream at the loss of their most successful marketing ploy, DTC advertising. Although painful and subject to major objections, my suggestions are worthy of major consideration. How can these entities legitimately object to requirements relating to efficacy, safety, and cost control?

My most important recommendation involves the utilization of evidence-based medicine. Not only would useless and potentially harmful medical activities be controlled, but eliminating them would be a major contribution of cost control. Before physicians endorse expensive diagnostic and therapeutic procedures in everyday medical care, they should assess evidence of their value and safety. The appropriate studies should be performed in advance by unbiased governmental and academic groups, financed for the function adequately. Again, entrepreneurial elements in our society would object to any expansion of government jurisdiction over their efforts. However, if we hope to rein in the frightful inflation occurring in healthcare, we must bite the bullet and do what is necessary. Such effort would prove its value in decades to come.

All of the above depends on a major change in belief of the American public about the ability of healthcare to affect their lives positively. If lay people continue to accept the notion that continued medical advances will be worth whatever they cost, the inflation of healthcare costs will continue unabated. The result will be some form of nationalized health insurance, in which the dimensions of the healthcare industry will be determined by governmental fiscal controls. It will require a phenomenal change in American thinking to make that form of healthcare rationing acceptable.

About the Author

Dr. Handler has had two distinct chapters in his career as a pathologist. The first is as a pathologist in a busy community hospital over a period of 40 years. In addition to routine pathology duties, he supervised the Continuing Medical Education Program for his entire career, started the Infection Control Committee, edited the Medical Staff Newsletter since its inception and crusaded for improved transfusion practices over a 30-year period.

His second role was in education at the University of Minnesota Medical School. He was intermittently responsible for the basic pathology course for first and second year medical students. The two careers complemented each other, both with particular emphasis on education.

In between these activities, he had time to contribute to the medical literature, emphasizing many of the tenets covered in this book. Since retirement from active practice, he has lectured for the Osher Lifelong Learning Institute, a function of the University of Minnesota. Last, and hopefully not least, he has been stimulated to put some of his controversial ideas on paper. Hence this book.